They Found the Unknown

THEY
FOUND
THE
UNKNOWN

*The stories of nine great discoveries
in the field of medical knowledge*

by *Robert Sidney Bowen*

MACRAE SMITH COMPANY: PHILADELPHIA

*In deep appreciation and with sincere thanks,
this book is dedicated to the wonderful staff of
the Onslow County Public Library,
Jacksonville, North Carolina.*

Contents

ONE: THE INVISIBLE EYE   11
Wilhelm Konrad Roentgen

TWO: PAIN GOES TO SLEEP   23
Crawford Williamson Long
William Thomas Green Morton

THREE: THE HIDDEN FLAME   39
Pierre Curie
Marie Sklodowska Curie

FOUR: THE LITTLE ANIMALS   61
Anton van Leeuwenhoek

FIVE: THE RED DEATH   83
Edward Jenner

SIX: MADNESS BY INFECTION   105
Louis Pasteur

SEVEN: THE YELLOW KILLER   125
Walter Reed

EIGHT: THE INVISIBLE MARAUDERS   145
Joseph Lister

NINE: THE MAGIC OF MOLD   167
Alexander Fleming
Howard Walter Florey

They Found the Unknown

1

The Invisible Eye

WILHELM KONRAD ROENTGEN
(1845–1923)

On the evening of November 8, 1895, two scientists were studying the light rays of a Crookes vacuum tube in the laboratory of the Department of Physics at Würzburg, Germany. One of the scientists was Wilhelm Konrad Roentgen, Director of Physics at Würzburg, and the other was his laboratory assistant.

The Crookes vacuum tube was a pear-shaped glass bulb from which all the air had been removed. Sealed into one side of the glass bulb was a positive electrode, and sealed into the opposite side was a negative electrode. Stretching between the two electrodes inside the

glass bulb was a strip of platinum. Wires from the electrodes ran to the terminal poles of an induction coil,
and it was connected by wires to some wet-cell batteries.

When the direct current of the wet-cell batteries was
turned on, the induction coil changed it to alternating
current and transmitted it to the Crookes vacuum tube.
As a result, the Crookes tube gave forth a yellowish-
green light that streaked the inside of the glass bulb
with flickering bands of color.

What type of rays of light emanated from the Crookes
vacuum tube no one had as yet found out. Other scientists were also conducting intensive studies of the strange
light, but thus far with no results of any scientific importance.

During the course of Roentgen's study and experiments, he had found out that when he coated a sheet of
paper with metallic salts, such as barium platino-cyanide,
and held it up to the light, the metallic salts coating
glowed with a weirdly glimmering fluorescence. He also
found out that no matter how far he held the coated
paper from the strange light the metallic salts still gave
forth the eerie, glimmering glow.

Why did the strange light coming from the Crookes
vacuum tube cause the metallic-salt-coated sheet of
paper to glow? Was it a single unknown ray of light that
caused the metallic salts to glow, or was it a combination
of several unknown light rays? Roentgen did not know
the answer, but as a scientist he knew there had to be
one, and he was determined to find it.

On impulse he switched off the wet-cell battery current, put the coated sheet of paper down on a nearby table, and turned on the laboratory lights.

"Let's cover the tube completely," he said to his assistant. "So that none of its light can show through. Then we will start from the beginning."

"I don't understand," the assistant said with a puzzled frown. "Just what do you mean, 'from the beginning?' "

"From total darkness, of course," Roentgen told him. "Then we will release the Crookes tube's light a little more at a time until we find just how much of the light is needed to make the metallic-salt-coated paper glow."

"And if the full intensity of the tube's light is needed?" the assistant murmured. "What then?"

Roentgen, who was by nature a gentle and unassuming man, smiled patiently.

"Then we will have at least found out that fact," he replied in his soft, quiet voice.

Taking a sheet of thin black cardboard, Roentgen cut it and folded it about the Crookes vacuum tube until he was sure no light would be able to shine through. That done, he then turned off all the laboratory lights, plunging the room into total darkness.

"I will now turn on the Crookes tube light," he said.

When Roentgen switched on the wet-cell battery current both men peered in the direction of the black, cardboard-covered Crookes vacuum tube. There was no light to be seen. Not even a thread of light leaking through a hair's-width opening in the black cardboard covering. There was nothing but darkness in the direction of their peering eyes.

[13]

Suddenly Roentgen stiffened and caught his breath.

"Do you notice anything?" he quickly asked his assistant. "Is there light coming from somewhere in the room, or are my eyes playing me tricks?"

The assistant did not reply for some moments, but when he did there was a note of awe in his voice.

"Yes, there is light somewhere!" he breathed. "A very faint glow, but it is not coming from the Crookes tube. That's completely covered and dark. It must be coming from somewhere else in the room. But how could it?"

"I don't know, but you are right," Roentgen said, as the excitement in him mounted. "It is a faint glow, and not coming from the Crookes tube. But it is here in this room somewhere. You search one side, while I search the other, and perhaps we can find where it is coming from."

Both scientists started moving slowly about their respective sides of the room, probing the darkness for the source of the faint glow of light they were now absolutely certain existed, but could not actually see. It did not seem to be coming from the ceiling, or the floor, or from any of the four walls. It was not stronger in one part of the room and weaker in another. As a matter of fact, it seemed to fill the entire room, and yet be no place.

After several minutes of searching and probing the darkness, Roentgen accidentally bumped against a table. Instinctively he grasped hold of the table to steady himself, and at the same time unconsciously lowered his searching eyes. It was then that he saw it, and the sight held him spellbound.

"Look, *look!*" he finally gasped.

His assistant came over to the table and saw it for himself. Roentgen had put the metallic-salt-coated sheet of paper down on the table when he cut the cardboard and fitted it about the Crookes vacuum tube, and it was this that was giving forth the glimmering glow! The mysterious, ghostly flicker was every bit as strong as it had been when Roentgen held it up to the full intensity of the vacuum tube's light.

The excitement in him causing his fingers to tremble slightly, Roentgen picked up the sheet of paper and turned it around so that the coated side faced away from the black, cardboard-covered Crookes tube. To his great surprise the coated side continued to glow just as strongly! Some kind of a ray of light, unknown to science and completely invisible to the human eye, was passing *through* the black cardboard over the Crookes tube, and also *through* the sheet of paper to make the metallic salts glow.

"It is uncanny!" The assistant's whisper presently broke the silence. "What in the world is causing it to do that?"

"Undoubtedly some kind of light ray coming from the tube," Roentgen murmured absently, staring at the glowing salts. "What type of ray I have no idea. Come, we will make some experiments, and perhaps learn more about it."

That evening of November 8, 1895, was the beginning. Then followed days and nights of intensive study and experimenting with the mysterious ray of light, which was invisible to the human eye.

Roentgen found out that when a piece of heavy metal was held between the covered Crookes tube and the metal-salt-coated paper, its shadow appeared on the paper. So did the shadow of a block of wood, and the shadow of a piece of hard rubber. The shadow of a deck of cards and sheets of tinfoil could be made to appear, and the greater the thickness of the sheets of tinfoil, the darker the shadow. The shadows of weights inside a box appeared on the coated paper, and even the needle inside an all-metal compass.

Of all the many experiments Roentgen conducted with the mysterious, invisible ray of light, two produced results of great interest and scientific significance. He found that when he held his hand between the covered Crookes tube and the coated paper the shadows of the bones showed clearly, and also the image of the hand itself. And, in addition, he found out that the invisible ray he had discovered affected photographic plates and film, so that he could take a picture of the bones in his hand—a picture he could develop and print to keep as a record!

After a month of intensive study, Roentgen wrote out a report of what he had found and sent it to the secretary of the Physical Medical Society of Würzburg. In January of 1896 he was invited to read his report at a meeting of the Society and conduct some experiments to bear out his claim. That was not because the members of the Society didn't believe what Roentgen had written to the secretary. They all knew him to be a quiet and modest man, who never exaggerated or boasted about his accomplishments. It was simply that in those days, as now, men of science demanded proof before they would accept anything as fact.

On January twenty-third, Roentgen appeared before the Society meeting with his equipment and read his report to the assembled members. The main paragraph read, "If the discharge of a fairly large induction coil be made to pass through a Crookes tube, the tube being covered with thin black cardboard, and if the whole apparatus be placed in a darkened room, there is observed at each discharge a brilliant illumination of a paper screen covered with barium platino-cyanide. The fluorescence thus produced being entirely independent of whether the plain or coated surface is turned toward the discharge tube."

When Roentgen had finished reading his report he conducted some of his experiments for the benefit of his audience. One of the experiments was to take a picture of the bones in the hand of Dr. Albert von Kölliker, a distinguished member of the Society. As it required half an hour to take and develop the picture, the time was spent by the Society members asking questions of Roentgen, and one of them was "What are you going to call these rays?"

Roentgen smiled and gave a little shake of his head.

"I do not know what the rays are," he replied quietly.

"But I had thought of calling them X-rays, X being the unknown quantity."

When the picture of Dr. Albert von Kölliker's hand bones was finally developed and shown to the Society's members, they were completely convinced of Roentgen's claim, and it was unanimously voted to call the new discovery "Roentgen's Rays."

The use of a photographic plate by Roentgen in his experiments before the Society meeting must have been cause for considerable chagrin among other scientists who were studying and experimenting with vacuum tubes at that time. Many of them who kept photographic plates in their laboratories had often found them to be fogged over and ruined when they went to use them. They would take the ruined plates to where they had bought them, claiming them to be of defective manufacture and demanding good ones in their place. If any of those scientists had but stopped to wonder why so many of his photographic plates had become ruined, and attempted to find out if there was any reason other than defective manufacture, he might have been the one to discover the invisible ray of light that was to become known as the X-ray.

For X-ray it was to become known, and not Roentgen's Rays, as the Physical Medical Society of Würzburg had unanimously voted to call the discovery. The reason for that was that on January sixth a Vienna newspaper printed a story of what Roentgen had found, calling it the X-ray, and by the time Roentgen read his report to the Society, newspapers all over the world had reprinted the Vienna paper's story. From then on, the discovery was to be the X-ray and almost never Roentgen's Rays.

The Vienna newspaper's story, however, was quite garbled and completely misleading as to what the X-ray really was, as well as just what could be done with it. As a result, countless thousands of nonmedical people all over the world got the impression that the mysterious X-ray could be used any place and at any time.

In no time at all the feminine world was angrily demanding that the use of such a ray be immediately outlawed. As a matter of fact, within a month after the announcement of Roentgen's discovery, a bill was introduced in the state legislature of New Jersey prohibiting the use of X-ray in opera glasses at theaters, or at any other places of public entertainment. And an English merchant (with a keen eye for new business) started advertising the sale of X-ray-proof clothing for both men and women.

To those outside the medical profession, the X-ray was soon regarded as something mysterious, fantastic and terrible. The idea of being able to look through flesh and see what was going on inside the body appealed to the imagination, but unfortunately in unfounded and frightening ways. There were people who imagined that the mysterious force called X-ray was capable of destroying whole cities and of creating all kinds of worldwide havoc. And there were others who imagined that anyone possessing the X-ray machine could look through the skull of a person and read his thoughts. One New

York newspaper reporter even wrote a story that a professor at Columbia University had found a way to imprint facts on the brains of his students by X-ray, and thus speed up their learning!

The medical world, though, was quick to understand and realize the advantages of the X-ray, and the practice of using X-ray equipment took hold at once. An apparatus to take X-ray pictures could easily be built for a cost of about one hundred dollars, and dealers in vacuum tubes and induction coils were swamped with orders. The X-ray was first used to locate bullets and foreign bodies in the flesh, and to detect fractured bones. It was used by army surgeons in the Greek-Turkish War in 1897, and it was also used in the Spanish-American War in 1898.

After he had read his report and conducted his experiments before the Physical Medical Society of Würzburg, Roentgen returned to his laboratory to perfect his X-ray apparatus and continue his studies and experiments. However, the wildly misleading publicity given the X-ray machine throughout the world affected him deeply. He was an extremely sensitive man, and the utterly fantastic stories going around and appearing in print about his X-ray machine bewildered and saddened him. In fact, they distressed him so much he shrank more and more from public view and became a virtual recluse in his laboratory.

High honors were bestowed on Roentgen for his great discovery, but receiving them must have been a painful ordeal for the scientist who now wanted only to hide himself away with his work. He was invited to Potsdam to dine with the German emperor and was given the title of Excellency. Streets were named after him, and he was awarded one of Germany's highest honors, the Order of the Royal Crown. Columbia University gave him a medal, and so did the Royal Society of England. Prince Ludwig of Bavaria made him a baron, and in 1901 he was awarded the Nobel Prize for Physics.

Roentgen being the kind of man he was, it never occurred to him to make money from his discovery. If he had patented his X-ray machine he would probably have amassed a huge fortune, but he never did. As far as he was concerned he had found something he believed would be of help to all mankind, and that was all he wanted. The only money he ever received from his discovery of the X-ray was the Nobel Prize.

Roentgen found and gave to the medical world a new and powerful weapon to use in its ceaseless battle against sickness and disease, but for him it brought mostly increasing heartache and sadness. World War I saddened him even more, and it also ruined him financially. In 1919, his beloved wife died, leaving him an unhappy and lonely old man. And to cap all his troubles, shortly before his death a malicious rumor was being circulated to the effect that it had really been his assistant who had discovered the X-ray.

Wilhelm Konrad Roentgen died in 1923, a penniless and broken man.

2

Pain Goes To Sleep

CRAWFORD WILLIAMSON LONG
(1815–1878)
WILLIAM THOMAS GREEN MORTON
(1819–1868)

Back in the year 1841 there lived in the small town of Jefferson, Georgia, a Dr. Crawford Williamson Long. He was a practicing physician, twenty-six years old, quite good-looking, and popular with the other young men in the community. As a matter of fact, one night a week the young men used to gather at Long's home, where they would discuss the topics of the day, play cards, and in general have a very enjoyable time.

In the winter of 1841 a traveling lecturer came to Jefferson to talk about the properties of nitrous oxide, a colorless gas that he called "Laughing Gas." Standing on the tailboard of his cart before his assembled audience, he inhaled some of the nitrous oxide gas from its rubber bag container, and almost immediately began to laugh heartily and act gay. He then invited some of the young men in the audience to come forward and also inhale the gas. Half a dozen did, and like the lecturer, they started laughing and cavorting about in high glee.

On that particular night Dr. Long was out in the country on one of his cases, and he missed the lecturer's visit. But his young friends told him about it at their next get-together. Those who had inhaled the laughing gas were most enthusiastic about the pleasant results, and they asked Dr. Long to make up some of the laughing gas so they might all have a happy time.

Long did not have any nitrous oxide in his office, nor the materials with which to manufacture it. However, when he was a medical student in Philadelphia he had once attended a chemical lecture and witnessed a somewhat similar demonstration conducted with ether. At that time ether was a medicine used only for nervous ailments, and in minute quantities because of its extremely unpleasant smell and taste.

Dr. Long did have some ether in his office, so he produced it and everybody took one or more good whiffs of its fumes. The effects were the same as those of nitrous oxide, and one and all had a pleasant time at the meeting. As a matter of fact, the ether whiffing was repeated at following get-togethers, and at such times Dr. Long noticed something that aroused his interest and curiosity.

He saw his friends, who were cavorting about the room, crash into heavy pieces of furniture, or collide with each other and fall to the floor, apparently without feeling any pain. When he asked his friends, they declared they indeed hadn't felt pain from their injuries. And when Dr. Long himself took a couple of bad falls he didn't feel any pain, either. More than once on a morning after a get-together he found ugly bruises on his body, but he would have no recollection at all of how or when they were caused.

As the lively parties in Dr. Long's home continued, one of the young men became bothered by two small tumors on the back of his neck. He spoke about them to Dr. Long, who said they would have to be cut out. The young man, however, refused to submit to the operation because he feared the pain of the surgical knife. It was, of course, true that through the centuries whenever a knife cut human flesh on the operating table, the result was agony for the patient. So the young man chose to keep his two small tumors rather than submit to the acute pain of Dr. Long's knife.

Some time afterward, though, Dr. Long got to thinking about how he and his young friends had hurt themselves while enjoying the effects of inhaled ether fumes, but had experienced no pain. And that started him wondering if by any chance the administering of ether to a patient would kill pain during an actual surgical operation. The more he thought about it, the more convinced he became that ether should be tried in such a situation. Finally, on the morning of March 30, 1842, he talked his young friend into submitting to a tumor operation while under the influence of ether.

The operating time was set for that afternoon in Dr. Long's home, and any of the young men's group who cared to attend were invited to do so. Dr. Long, however, wanted at least one man of high standing in the community to be present as a witness, so he persuaded the principal of Jefferson Academy to attend also.

When all was ready, Dr. Long poured some drops of ether on a towel and held the towel over the young patient's nose. He kept track of the patient's pulse, and when the young man made no move or outcry when pricked with a pin, the doctor picked up his surgical knife and removed the two small tumors. When the operation was completed and the ether-soaked towel removed, the patient quickly recovered full consciousness and declared he had felt no pain at all. In fact, he had to be shown the tumors to be convinced they had actually been removed.

If Dr. Long had written up an account of that tumor operation and sent it to any of the medical journals for publication, he would undoubtedly have gone down in medical history as the officially recognized discoverer of how to eliminate pain from surgery. Unfortunately for him, he did not. He had studied medicine under a Dr. George B. Wood, who was very strongly opposed to the premature publication of medical discoveries, and of the firm conviction that a one-time experiment, even though successful, proved nothing. Naturally Dr. Long believed what his teacher had taught him, and so he simply wrote about the operation in his diary and let it go at that.

As a matter of fact, although Dr. Long had been successful in his first attempt at using ether to kill pain during an operation, he did not seek a second or third success. And for good reason.

In spite of the fact that the principal of Jefferson Academy had been a witness to the operation, the older and more distinguished doctors in the region considered Long's claims utterly ridiculous, and publicly declared that if he continued the practice of using ether when operating, he would sooner or later kill one of his patients. Very soon, rumors started circulating that he was simply carving up people in their sleep. As a result he became very unpopular, and sick people were afraid to go to him. In addition, he received several threats that if one of his patients did die he would be lynched.

And so, although a man of medicine found a way to cause the death of pain on an operating table in 1842, that great discovery was to remain unrevealed to the rest of the world for another four years.

One evening in December, 1844, Horace Wells, a dentist who lived and practiced in Hartford, Connecticut, read a notice in the newspaper of a lecture on nitrous oxide, the "laughing gas," to be given that night at Union Hall by a man who called himself Professor

[27]

Gardner Q. Colton. One-night-stand lectures were quite popular in those days, and as the subject of this one interested Dr. Wells, he attended.

"Professor" Colton delivered a short talk on the properties of nitrous oxide, and then invited anybody in the audience to come up on the stage and experience the happy effects of his laughing gas when inhaled from a rubber bag container. Dr. Wells was one of those who went up on the stage, and he had the same experience Long had had two years before. He saw grown men hurt themselves as they pranced gaily about, and when asked, declare they had felt no pain. Wells even injured himself, cutting his leg during a fall, but he did not feel any pain until the effects of the gas had worn off.

That experience, for Dr. Wells, was like a great white light shining into the darkness. Was this not a way for him to eliminate pain when extracting teeth?

After the lecture, Dr. Wells went to Professor Colton and got him to agree to bring a bag of nitrous oxide gas to his dental office the next morning. The dentist had a bad wisdom tooth that was starting to give him some trouble and he wanted to test out his theory of no pain by having it extracted while he was under the influence of nitrous oxide gas.

The next morning Professor Colton appeared with his bag of nitrous oxide gas, and administered the gas to Wells until he lapsed into a state of unconsciousness. Then Wells' assistant, John Mankey Riggs, extracted the bothersome wisdom tooth without his experiencing any pain at all.

Highly elated by the success of the experiment, Dr. Wells then obtained the materials to manufacture nitrous oxide and began using it in his dental practice. He used it on some fifteen patients, but not with very much success. In the majority of cases the patient laughed so heartily and became so violent in his movements that it was almost impossible for Dr. Wells to keep him in the dentist's chair long enough to extract the tooth.

The failures, however, did not discourage him. Nitrous oxide had worked perfectly on him, and he was sure that it could be made to work successfully on others. Not only that; he felt sure his discovery could also be used to eliminate pain on the hospital operating table.

It so happened that an old friend and former dental associate of his, one William Thomas Green Morton, was then attending Harvard Medical School to obtain his M.D. degree. So Wells took a trip to Boston to tell his old friend of his discovery. He asked Dr. Morton to use his influence with Dr. John Collins Warren, of the Massachusetts General Hospital, to obtain permission for a demonstration. He offered to extract a tooth of some volunteer in Dr. Warren's surgery class.

Dr. Warren did grant the permission requested, and a member of his class volunteered for the demonstration; but unfortunately for Wells, the demonstration was a complete failure.

Perhaps the dentist administered too little of the nitrous oxide gas, or perhaps he didn't wait long enough for it to take maximum effect. At any rate, when he clamped his forceps about the volunteer's tooth and started to pull, the volunteer let out a yell of pain. The members of Warren's class who had assembled to witness the demonstration started to jeer and shout "Humbug!" and Dr. Wells was virtually thrown out of the hospital.

He returned to Hartford smarting with shame and completely crestfallen by his failure to prove that surgical operations could be performed without pain to the patient. However, even though his failure had made him a laughingstock at Massachusetts General Hospital, he still had faith in his discovery and continued to administer nitrous oxide gas on occasion to his dental patients.

Up in Boston, meanwhile, Dr. Morton was conducting extensive experiments in an attempt to meet with success where his old friend had met with failure. He was convinced that Wells was on the track of something of great importance, but was not using the right materials or the right methods to attain his goal. An acquaintance of Dr. Morton's, a Dr. Charles Thomas Jackson, who was a well-known chemist and geologist, had told him that sulphuric ether, which was pure ether, would be far more reliable and effective in putting a patient into a state of unconsciousness than nitrous oxide.

Armed with that new knowledge, Dr. Morton went to a drugstore and bought a bottle of sulphuric ether. Taking it to his home, he experimented first with his dog. He poured a few drops of the pure ether on a cloth and held it over the dog's nose. When he believed the dog to be in an unconscious state he removed the cloth and waited. The dog did not move for some minutes, but presently he awoke slowly from sleep to shake himself vigorously and go bounding away.

The experiment on the dog apparently successful, Doctor Morton then tried it on himself. But he had read in a medical textbook that pure ether could be very dangerous if not handled properly, so he put only a few drops on the cloth he applied to his own nose. As a result he slipped into a state of only semi-unconsciousness and came out of it with a splitting headache.

He tried again, and this time used more ether. He experienced a numbness creeping through his body just before he passed into a state of unconsciousness. And when he regained consciousness his entire body was numb and without feeling. That alarmed him, but eventually the numbness went away and he was quite all right again. For him, that second experiment was a complete success. He had proved to himself that a person could be put into a state of total unconsciousness by the administering of sulphuric ether and fully recover in a relatively short time.

Although Dr. Morton was studying for his M.D., he was also practicing dentistry at the same time. And so he started using ether to kill pain during tooth extraction, but not with the degree of success he had expected. In some cases, the use of ether on a patient produced only a lengthy vomiting spell; and in other cases the patient became only extremely drowsy, and not fully unconscious.

Those experiences led Morton to believe it was the method of administering the ether that was at fault, and not the sulphuric ether itself. So he went to a distinguished naturalist friend of his, a Dr. A. A. Gould, and asked him to design an apparatus for controlled administering of ether. Dr. Gould drew up a design that had valves to regulate the flow of the patient's breath, and Dr. Morton went away convinced that he could now lick his problem.

He had a machinist build an apparatus of Dr. Gould's design, and when tests proved it to be effective he reached for the big goal he had been aiming at ever since Dr. Wells' failure. He went again to Massachusetts General Hospital to see Dr. John Collins Warren. But this time it was to get the famous surgeon's permission for his own demonstration of how pain could be eliminated from hospital surgery. Dr. Warren granted permission and named a day and time when he would be performing an operation.

The appointed day arrived, October 16, 1846, and as the time for the demonstration drew near the operating theater was filled with students, doctors and other interested people who had come to watch. But there was no sign of Dr. Morton. When the time to begin the operation arrived and Dr. Morton had still not put in an appearance, Dr. Warren announced that Dr. Morton had probably changed his mind and got ready to perform the operation in the usual manner.

At the very last moment, though, Dr. Morton burst breathlessly into the operating theater. He had stopped at a machinist's shop to have a new part fitted to his ether-administering apparatus, and it had taken considerably longer than he'd expected. He apologized to Dr. Warren, who stepped back from the operating table and told him to proceed with his demonstration.

Dr. Morton set up his apparatus and administered ether to the patient, and when the patient became unconscious he moved aside so that Dr. Warren could proceed with the operation. At no time did the patient move or utter a sound. When the operation was over and the patient fully recovered from the effects of the ether, he stated that he had not felt any pain. All he had felt was a faint scraping sensation at the back of his neck just before he became unconscious.

The success of Dr. Morton's demonstration at Massachusetts General Hospital received immediate acclaim throughout the medical world. And the famous physician, scholar and author Oliver Wendell Holmes, Sr., gave three names to the discovery. *Anesthesia* for the state of unconsciousness obtained, *anesthetic* for the preparation administered, and *anesthetist* for the one who administers it. October 16, 1848, was a day of great triumph for Dr. William Thomas Green Morton, but it was also the beginning of a series of events none of which were to favor or benefit him at all.

The first thing to happen was that the doctors at Massachusetts General refused to use Morton's services in any more operations unless he told them what his anesthetic preparation was. But Morton wanted to keep that his secret, because if he told them it was simply sulphuric ether he would no longer have exclusive use of it.

[33]

By then he had visions of patenting his apparatus and making a fortune for himself from the sales of it to doctors, dentists and hospitals, all over the world. In fact, he was already spending every penny he had, and all he could borrow, on building up a worldwide sales organization. On the other hand, if he refused to reveal his secret to the doctors of Massachusetts General, he might possibly arouse their anger and—perhaps even more important—their suspicion of his professional ethics. Adverse publicity coming out of such a situation could well ruin him before he even got started on making his fortune.

It was a dilemma that caused him much worry and loss of sleep, but he eventually decided to get his patent papers filed in Washington first, and then tell the doctors of Massachusetts General his secret. When the preparation secret was revealed it was written up by a member of the Massachusetts General staff and published in the *Boston Medical and Surgical Journal.* And that was when, to use an expression, the balloon really went up!

Down in Jefferson, Georgia, Dr. Crawford Williamson Long read the article and quickly voiced his claim that it was he and not Dr. Morton who was the first to use an anesthetic for a surgical operation. He produced his diary account of the tumor operation he had performed in 1842. He also wrote to his senator in Washington making his claim for the credit, stating that he did not want any money for it, but simply official recognition.

When Dr. Charles Thomas Jackson heard the news, he rushed forward, claiming that he should be given the credit, because it was he who had suggested to Dr. Morton that he use sulphuric ether. He even produced two witnesses who swore they heard Dr. Jackson make the suggestion and also heard Dr. Morton say he had not known of sulphuric ether until Dr. Jackson told him about it.

Even Dr. Horace Wells jumped into the bitter controversy. He claimed that he had been using both nitrous oxide and sulphuric ether in his dental practice long before Dr. Morton's triumph at Massachusetts General Hospital. Therefore, to him should go official recognition as the discoverer of the principle of anesthesia.

In no time at all what was to become known as the Ether War was being furiously waged in Congress and in the press. There were claims and counterclaims, suits and countersuits, but with nothing being decided officially. It went on for years, and people got sick and tired of hearing about it.

During those years Morton worked day and night perfecting his apparatus, building up a world-wide sales organization, and fighting tooth and nail to gain official credit for the discovery. He tried to get the Army and Navy to purchase his apparatus, but with no success. Both the Army and Navy Departments ruled against it, although many Army and Navy surgeons did start using ether as a surgical anesthetic.

As a matter of fact, so did countless civilian surgeons, doctors and dentists throughout the world. And they proved they did not need Dr. Morton's fancy, patented apparatus. They simply applied the correct number of drops of ether to a towel or a cloth cone over the patient's nose and waited the necessary length of time for him to become unconscious before proceeding with the operation.

In time, Morton's world-wide sales organization collapsed from a lack of business, and he went plunging headlong toward financial ruin. The strain began to affect his health, too, although he continued to fight for official recognition. The Ether War more or less faded away, with no one the victor. It was the general opinion of medical men that Dr. Long and Dr. Morton deserved joint credit for the great discovery, but there was never any official credit given to anyone.

Eventually tragic death removed all four combatants from the Ether War.

By January of 1848 Dr. Horace Wells had turned to experimenting with chloroform as an effective anesthetic, but the bitter events of the past four years preyed too heavily on his mind. On the twenty-fourth day of that month he inhaled too deeply of the chloroform fumes and slashed an artery with a razor just before he sank into unconsciousness to die.

On July 15, 1868, Dr. William Thomas Green Morton, his health and mind by then seriously affected by his desperate struggle to gain official recognition of his claimed discovery, was advised to undergo medical treatment, but refused. Instead, he rushed out of his New York City home to jump into his carriage and drive furiously through Central Park. Suddenly he jumped out of the carriage, ran a few steps, and fell to the ground unconscious. He was carried to a nearby hospital, but died a few hours later.

On June 16, 1878, Dr. Crawford Williamson Long administered ether to a woman patient for the delivery of her baby. Seconds after the baby was born and Doctor Long had handed it to an attending nurse, he collapsed to the floor with a stroke and died shortly afterward.

Dr. Charles Thomas Jackson outlived the other three Ether War combatants, but in 1873 he was committed to an insane asylum. He died there on August 28, 1880, seven years later.

Perhaps the most amazing thing of all connected with the rather bizarre story of anesthesia is that in 1800 when an Englishman, Sir Humphrey Davy, discovered nitrous oxide, he wrote, "As nitrous oxide in its extensive operation seems capable of destroying physical pain, it may probably be used with advantage in surgical operations in which no great effusion of blood takes place."

Those words were published in several books of medicine used by doctors and surgeons for study and research, yet thousands of men, women and children were to suffer agonies of pain on hospital operating tables for almost half a century before anyone did anything about Sir Humphrey's suggestion!

3

The Hidden Flame

PIERRE CURIE
(1859–1906)
MARIE SKLODOWSKA CURIE
(1867–1934)

In the living room of a rather sparsely furnished flat on
the Boulevard Kellermann in Paris, France, a man sat
busily writing at a desk. Across the room from him in
a chair by a table a woman sat busily sewing on a baby's
dress.

The man was Pierre Curie. Tall and dark, with a lean
face and a rough beard, thirty-eight years old, he was a
distinguished French physicist, who taught at the School
of Physics in Paris. The writing he was doing was a lecture he was to deliver to his class the next day.

They Found the Unknown

The woman was his wife, Marie, who had been born Manya Sklodowska, in Warsaw, Poland. Thirty years old, Marie was inches shorter and not nearly as thin as her husband. She had ashen gray eyes, a high, curving forehead and rather severely combed fair hair. Also a physicist, she was not at the moment as well known as her husband. However she did hold two university degrees and a fellowship, and had written a special treatise on the magnetization of tempered steel. The dress she was sewing was for their two-months-old daughter, Irene, asleep in the next room.

The time was a November evening in 1897. Although neither of them dreamed it, that evening was to mark the beginning of a long and heart-breaking climb to a pinnacle of scientific fame few others have attained, before or since.

As Pierre Curie finished the sentence he was writing he glanced up just in time to see his wife put aside her sewing and pick up a pamphlet on the table beside her. A warm smile touched his lips when he saw a faint frown of studied concentration knit her brows as she read the pamphlet. Presently he broke the silence in the room. "Have you chosen your subject yet?"

Marie Curie looked up from her reading with a hesitant smile. "What did you say, Pierre?"

"Have you decided on a subject of research to do a thesis on for your doctor's degree?" Curie asked.

"Not yet," his wife replied slowly, frowning again. "What would you suggest?"

Pierre Curie gave a little laugh and wigwagged a

[40]

finger. "Exactly what you decide upon, my dear," he said. "What is that you're reading?"

"A recent publication by Henri Becquerel," Marie Curie said, touching the pamphlet. "He's been making some very interesting experiments with salts of uranium. But, perhaps you've read this?"

"No, I've only glanced at it," Curie said with a shake of his head. "What results did he get?"

"Some rather puzzling ones," his wife replied, returning her eyes to the pamphlet. "He started out to determine if there were rays, like Roentgen's X-ray, that were radiated by fluorescent bodies coming in contact with light. But what he found out was that light had nothing to do with the emitting of the rays. He found out that uranium salts that were not exposed to light spontaneously gave forth some rays of an unknown nature."

Marie Curie paused for a moment to study a page of the pamphlet and then went on speaking.

"He put a compound of uranium on a photographic plate completely wrapped in black paper," she said, "and found that an impression was made on the plate through the black paper. And also that the unknown rays sent out by the uranium salts made the surrounding air a conductor. To make certain that it was not previous exposure to light that caused the uranium compound to give off these unknown rays, he kept some in total darkness for several months and then tried the experiment. The result was the same. The compound of uranium still radiated some unknown rays."

"What does he believe the nature of the radiation to be?" Pierre Curie asked. "And its exact source?"

Marie Curie shook her head. "He has no idea," she said. "Both are still a mystery."

Pierre Curie smiled and leaned forward. "So now you do have a subject of research for your doctor's degree thesis," he said softly.

She didn't speak for a moment, but stared fixedly down at the pamphlet, deep in thought. Then she looked over at him. "Where does that tiny bit of energy come from?" she said in a low voice, as though asking only herself the question. "And what can be the nature of its radiation? And . . ."

She paused and smiled almost shyly. "It is a whole new field to explore," she said softly. "Will you help me, Pierre?"

Curie got up and went over to bend down and kiss her lightly on the cheek. "That is a completely unnecessary question, my dear," he said, and kissed her cheek again.

For Marie Curie to decide to seek the answers to the questions created by Henri Becquerel's experiments was one thing, but to set about the task was something entirely different. For one thing there was the matter of finding a suitable place where she could conduct her research work. And for another, there was the matter of securing the highly sensitive precision instruments that were necessary.

As it turned out, Pierre Curie was able to help her in solving both of those initial problems. He spoke to the head of the School of Physics and got permission for her to use a small glassed-in room on the second floor. It was by no means ideal for her work, because it was damp and cold and half filled with unused equipment for other types of scientific work. But it was the only thing offered her, and so it had to do. The equipment Pierre was able to give her consisted of a few pieces he had designed himself, for use in his own work, and some designed by his brother, Jacques, who was also a well-known physicist.

When she was finally settled in her somewhat mis-named "laboratory," Marie Curie began her research work by measuring the power of the mysterious compound of uranium rays to make the surrounding air a conductor of electricity, and after some weeks she obtained her first results of the experiments. They were that the power of the rays was in proportion to the amount of uranium used in the tests, and that they were not affected by such things as temperature and light.

Encouraged by what she had learned from her series of tests and experiments, Marie Curie then began a long series of tests to find out if uranium was the only chemical element capable of giving off the mysterious rays. In other words, had it been just by mere chance that Henri Becquerel selected for his tests the only chemical element—uranium—that gave off the mysterious rays, or did the radiation also exist in other chemical elements?

To answer that question Marie carefully examined and tested all known chemical bodies, both in a pure state and in compounds, and discovered that uranium was not the only chemical element that would produce the mysterious rays. She discovered that another element, called thorium, gave forth the strange rays or produced "radioactivity," as she termed it.

With that important step behind her, she then started to find out if radioactivity was limited only to simple chemical elements, or if it was also to be found in minerals. To do this work she enlisted the help of her husband, who obtained permission to borrow a number of mineral samples from the collection owned by the School of Physics. And the results of her test were what she had expected. The mineral samples that did not contain uranium or thorium were inactive. Only samples containing uranium or thorium produced the rays. In other words, it seemed as if they alone were radioactive minerals.

Oddly enough, when she made the above-mentioned discovery Marie Curie also discovered something which completely baffled her and caused her and her husband to consider the possibility that somewhere along the line she had made a mistake in her findings. The reason such a thought arose was because when she started measuring the radioactivity of minerals containing uranium or thorium she found out that the radioactivity produced by the mineral being measured was much more powerful than should be expected from the amount of uranium or thorium that was in that particular sample.

The strength of the radioactivity should have been in proportion to the amount of uranium or thorium, but it wasn't. So it naturally followed that somewhere a mistake had been made. However, no mistake had been made, for when Marie Curie started her measurement tests all over again, and checked and re-checked, the same cold fact was the result in every single case. The amount of uranium or thorium in a mineral sample *had nothing to do with the strength of the radioactivity it produced.*

After more tests and many consultations with her husband, Marie Curie decided there could be but one answer. There had been no mistake made. It was not uranium or thorium that produced the unknown and mysterious rays but a much more powerful radioactive substance. And as she had thoroughly tested all known chemical elements, what she had discovered must be an entirely new element, whose existence had remained hidden, until now, since the beginning of time.

The discovery of this powerful new element was a tremendous triumph of achievement for Marie Curie, and particularly so because of the conditions under which she made it. The room loaned her by the School of Physics was so cold and damp that frequently her fingers were almost too numbed to operate her delicate instruments. And with no money to buy more elaborate instruments, she was often forced to duplicate her tests again and again to make sure that the only instruments she did have were really telling her the truth. Added to her daylight hours, and often nighttime hours, of concentrated effort in the cold and damp room were the not-so-small tasks of being an efficient housewife and mother to her infant daughter.

But the discovery of a brand-new chemical element had been made, and that was more than enough to make Marie Curie shrug aside all the trials and tribulations she had been forced to suffer in the process. Now for the next step. The new element did exist—that she knew from her exhaustive tests. Now she must find it, bring it into the light, examine it thoroughly, and give it a name.

The next step—actually many, many, small, painstaking steps—was not to be taken by Marie Curie alone. Up to this point Pierre Curie had been giving help to his wife in such ways as getting her the room at the School of Physics, giving her the few instruments he and his brother had designed, and giving her advice and encouragement whenever she needed it. He had devoted most of his attention to an exhaustive study of crystals he was making, but now he put that aside and gave her one hundred per cent cooperation and assistance. It now became the team of Marie and Pierre Curie that was attempting the arduous task of finding the new and mysterious unnamed element.

It was in June of 1898 that the team of Marie and Pierre Curie went into action, and it was to remain a team, with neither contributing any more than the other, until tragic death broke it up in 1906.

In July of 1898 Marie and Pierre Curie prepared a paper that was read before the French Academy of Sciences. They stated that in pitchblende, an ore of uranium, there was radioactivity to be found. They called it Becquerel rays. These rays, they had discovered, were

[46]

far more radioactive than those of uranium and thorium alone, and so it was their firm belief that they came from an entirely new element in the mineral.

The news that the Curies were on the track of an element brand new to science was not exactly enthusiastically received by the scientific world. To say the most, it was received with only mild interest, and none of the great scientific minds was impressed in the slightest. As had happened dozens of times before the Curies, when a relative unknown was on the threshold of a great discovery the general comment was, "Give us something we can see and touch and examine, and then we will consider the truth of your claims."

The Curies, however, were not daunted by what others thought and said. They were both convinced that a brand-new element did exist, and all that mattered to them was its finding. So they set about searching for it in pitchblende in its crude state, instead of the pure oxide of uranium extracted from it, because they discovered, after some more tests, that pitchblende in its crude state was four times more radioactive.

The procedure they followed was a process of scientific elimination. By chemical analysis they separated all the elements in pitchblende one by one, and tested each for its radioactive strength. And eventually they narrowed their search down to two separate parts of the composition of pitchblende. These two parts showed radioactivity of a far greater strength than any of the other parts, and that fact clearly indicated to them that they were on the track of not just one new element, but two!

Spurred on by the prospect of a double goal, they presently managed to isolate one of the unknown elements and determine that its analytical properties were in part related to the properties to be found in bismuth. But it was a new metal, unknown to the world until that month of July in 1898 when they discovered it, and so of course it should be given a name.

Pierre Curie suggested that his wife select a name, and after a brief moment of hesitation she said she would like to name it *polonium* in honor of the country of her birth. Although Marie had come to Paris from Poland in 1891 to study at the Sorbonne, and four years later had married a Frenchman, an intense love of her native land, long captive under Russian and German oppression, was always in her heart. And so, with the wholehearted agreement of her husband and co-discoverer, Marie Curie named the new metal polonium, and a paper announcing its discovery was written and read before the Academy of Sciences later that month.

With polonium discovered, analyzed and named, and its existence made known to the scientific world, the Curies set to work to make their second discovery—find "that other one" as they called it. And they did. In December of 1898 they announced they had found that a second new and unknown element in pitchblende did exist, and they proposed to call it *radium* because of its powerful radioactivity.

Radium?

The announcement by Pierre and Marie Curie that they had discovered another new element that they called radium was, if anything, less enthusiastically received by the scientific world than had been their original announcement that ore of uranium contained a mysterious, unknown, radioactive element. Although physicists and chemists respected the Curies and were interested in their work, they simply could not accept their claim for fact. If it was fact, it turned a whole lot of already acquired knowledge upside down. It contradicted a lot of scientific beliefs that were widely accepted as absolute proof. If there was such a thing as radium, what did it look like? What was its atomic weight? And a hundred other ifs, ands, and buts!

In short, the scientific world more or less said, "Show us, and prove it, and then maybe we'll believe."

In order to convince the interested but highly skeptical scientific world, it now became necessary for the Curies to obtain pure radium that could actually be seen, and measure its atomic weight, and so forth. What they had found had been only imperceptible traces of the element that were far too minute to be seen with the eye, let alone measured for atomic weight.

This task, however, presented problems so overwhelming to Pierre and Marie Curie that at first they seriously doubted they would ever get the chance even to begin it. For one thing, though they now knew how to isolate radium in pitchblende, they would need a tremendous quantity of the ore to be able to extract enough radium to be seen and measured. For another thing, pitchblende was costly, and what they would have to pay for the amount of it they needed was much, much more than the amount of money they had in their meager savings. Was it possible to buy it from the St. Joachimsthal mines in Bohemia, where its uranium salts were extracted and used in the making of glass? The cost of just shipping the ore from the St. Joachimsthal mines to Paris would be almost as much as the total of their savings.

For days they studied their problems from every angle, hoping and praying to find some way they could surmount them, at least enough to let them make a start. But it was all to no avail. The high wall barring the way to their goal remained unscalable.

"It's hopeless, and unfair!" Marie Curie said bitterly one night, as she and her husband sat alone in their living room. "We know we have found it, but we can't prove it. It would cost money, and we are too poor!"

Pierre Curie, seated at his desk, nodded sadly. He started to sigh, but checked it as the germ of a thought slipped into his mind. "Wait a minute, my dear!" he breathed. "Perhaps not!"

"Perhaps we are not too poor?" his wife questioned in startled amazement. "You mean . . . ?"

"No, no." He stopped her with a quick gesture. "I mean that perhaps there is a chance of getting the pitchblende, and getting it for a price we will be able to pay."

Marie Curie gave him a bewildered look. "But we know the price of the ore is——"

"Exactly!" Pierre Curie stopped her again. "We know the price of crude pitchblende, but what about the residue after they have extracted the uranium salts for glass-making? I'm sure they must have mountains of the stuff that's no longer of any use to them, and they'd probably accept a very low price from anyone who wanted to cart it away."

"Of course!" Marie Curie exclaimed as great excitement lighted up her face. "I see what you mean. There would be lots of traces of radium to be found in the residue of the crude ore. Pierre, that is a way for us!"

The Curies went to bed happy and full of plans that night. And the next day they got in touch with an Austrian physicist who was a friend of theirs and asked him to find out from the owner of the St. Joachimsthal mines if it would be possible for them to buy a large quantity of the pitchblende residue at a reasonable price. A few days later their Austrian friend notified them that they could buy large quantities of the pitchblende residue, and at a price they could afford.

That news was the first step they took on a four-year journey.

The next step was to find a place big enough and well enough equipped for the gigantic task ahead of them. The cold, damp room at the School of Physics was not suitable at all, and they searched fruitlessly elsewhere. However, the room in the School of Physics faced a courtyard, and on the other side of the courtyard was a wooden shack and an old shed with a skylight. The roofs of these buildings were so battered by time and weather that rain would come right on through. In fact, the buildings were so utterly useless for the School's purposes, that the Curies had no trouble at all in obtaining permission to use them, along with the courtyard and the second-story room they had already been using.

Happy to have some place where they could do their work, even though it was a far cry from what they had hoped to get, the Curies went to work fixing it up as best they could. And a few days later they met with some good luck which compensated a little for the terrible condition of their working quarters. They heard from their Austrian friend that one ton of pitchblende residue was on the way, and, best of all, that they would not have to pay for it. A professor at the Academy of Science in Vienna, upon hearing of their work, had persuaded the Austrian Government, the actual owner of the St. Joachimsthal mines, to make a gift to the Curies of their first ton of residue. All they had to do was pay the shipping charge, which they were able to afford.

A week or so later a huge truck piled high with bags of pitchblende residue pulled into the courtyard of their working quarters, and they began their Herculean task. They were happy and excited and filled with unshakable determination to attain their elusive goal. But it was not always to be like that with them. As the days became weeks and then months, and even years, they were often to wonder if they really would be able to isolate enough radium to prove their claim, or if they were searching for something so infinitesimal it could as well be nothing.

The pitiful amount of equipment available to them was a constant drawback to making rapid progress. And the weather was perhaps their worst enemy of all. Because the shed and the shack had no chimneys to carry off the smoke and gases from their pieces of boiling and heating equipment, they had to do that part of the work in the courtyard. But rain in summer, and snow and sleet in winter, would drive them inside with their equipment, where they had to go on working with choking throats and streaming eyes. Half the time it was so unbearably hot inside that they were ready to collapse, and the other half of the time it was so raw and chilly they could hardly work.

The first year was spent concentrating on extracting from the mass of pitchblende residue all the elements that showed radioactivity, then testing and measuring to determine which ones produced the greatest amount of the mysterious rays. Again and again they were forced to repeat some step in their work because of insufficient equipment or bad weather.

For long periods of time they would both work at some particular job; then each would work at a separate job; then they would alternate jobs. From the first year right through the fourth, however, they were a team at work. No matter what either of them did, it was as a step toward their common goal. And although they often experienced frustration, heartbreak, and even torturing doubt, their burning determination to achieve their goal never slackened for an instant. They knew their radium existed, and they were determined to isolate enough of it to prove their claim, if it took them the rest of their lives!

In a general sense their four-year task was smelting

and boiling down, pouring off liquids, extracting and measuring, checking and re-checking, and a dozen other procedures, and that infinitesimal thing they sought to isolate continually hid itself from them. But not forever. Eventually came the day when their patient struggle paid off and they were able to isolate a sufficient amount of pure radium to prove their claim.

One evening of the forty-fifth month after they had started their great task, they came home from their work dead tired but keyed up with excitement, for they both knew the end was in sight. It wouldn't be long before they would have their victory—not long now before they would be able to see their new element in its pure state.

As they had a thousand times before that evening, they talked about their work during dinner, and afterward when Marie Curie had put little Irene to bed. The hands of the living room clock crept around to nine, and they knew they should go to bed to get the rest they needed for tomorrow's work, but each was reluctant to make the first move. They were too keyed up to sleep. As a matter of fact, each of them secretly wanted to go back to the shed in the School of Physics courtyard just to see if everything was going along all right, and if something had taken place since they'd left.

"I wonder what it will look like," Marie Curie presently broke a few moments of musing silence between them. "What color, I mean."

Her husband smiled and lifted a shoulder.

"Who can say?" he murmured. "Perhaps a whole rainbow of colors. Would that please you?"

"Very much," Marie Curie said with a little laugh. "But even one color would do. If it was beautiful enough."

"I believe I'd like red," Pierre Curie said, and absently rearranged some papers on his desk for perhaps the tenth time. "A wild, flaming red. With perhaps streaks of vivid orange running through it."

Marie Curie glanced at him sharply, and instantly knew that while his tongue made idle conversation his thoughts were elsewhere. The same place as her own. She leaned forward with an eager expression on her tired face.

"Pierre?"

"Yes, my dear?"

"Do you feel very sleepy?" Marie Curie asked.

The shadow of a smile touched Pierre Curie's mouth.

"As a matter of fact, I don't feel sleepy in the slightest," he replied. "Why?"

Marie Curie hesitated and seemed to square her shoulders.

"I'd like to go over there just to look in for a bit," she finally said. "Wouldn't you?"

Her husband laughed and got quickly to his feet. "Very much, my dear!" he exclaimed. "So, shall we?"

After speaking to Pierre Curie's father, who was then living with them, they went out of the house and hurried through the streets almost like two eager children head-ing for a surprise party. As they neared the School of Physics, located on Rue Lhomond, they slowed their pace for some mysterious reason they did not understand, or try to. And when they walked across the courtyard to the battered old shed, where they had virtually lived for the past four years, they almost moved on tiptoe.

Pierre Curie opened the door with his key, and they went inside. Curie started to light the lamp, but before he could even strike a match his wife grasped his arm.

"No, don't!" she said in a breathless voice. Then, an instant later, "Pierre . . . look!"

He did not have to ask "at what?" In that same moment he, too, was looking at the faintly bluish phosphorescent light that rose up out of a huge smelting vat and glowed from the little glass tubes on a nearby table. There at the bottom of the vat and in the many little glass tubes was their four-year goal and their victory— at long last enough pure radium to prove to the whole scientific world what they had truly believed to be fact from the very beginning.

For several moments they did not speak, for there were no words to be spoken in this moment of great triumph. They could only stand there and gaze in wonder and awe at the delicately tinted glow that seemed to flow out and touch every corner of the room.

"Our radium, Pierre!" Marie Curie whispered presently. "And it *is* beautiful!"

Curie didn't say anything. He simply bent his head and kissed her tenderly.

THE HIDDEN FLAME

The battle was won. The Curies were able to prepare one decigram of pure radium and determine its atomic weight. The men of the scientific world were forced to admit that Pierre and Marie Curie had proved their claim with incontestable facts, and the news of their great victory was widely acclaimed.

Yes, the battle to prove the existence of radium to the scientific world had been won, but there was still a tremendous amount of work for Pierre and Marie Curie to do. Countless papers on their research work and its results had to be written and published. But most important of all, an exhaustive study had to be made of this new-found wonder to find out everything possible about it—how it was made up, how and for what it could be used, and hundreds of other questions that are still unanswered.

Scientists all over the world joined the Curies in seeking out the answers to the countless riddles, and long before they were through, they all knew that Pierre and Marie Curie had made one of the most valuable discoveries in the history of the world—valuable in price because a single gram of it was worth $150,000, and valuable to mankind because of all the wonderful things it could do. There were many uses, but perhaps the greatest was help in the curing of cancer.

For four years after their great discovery Pierre and Marie Curie continued working together with their "baby," radium. And then, on April 16, 1906, tragedy struck and they were together no more.

On the afternoon of that day Pierre Curie was walking along a narrow street filled with traffic, and his thoughts, presumably, were occupied with other matters. At any rate, he suddenly started over to the other side of the street just as a heavy wagon drawn by two horses came rumbling along. Unable to stop in time, Pierre walked into one of the horses, who reared and knocked him down, and before the driver could stop his wagon the heavy wheels had rolled over Pierre Curie and crushed the life out of him.

The death of Pierre Curie left his wife with two small daughters, very little money, and an aching, empty heart. Perhaps another woman would have turned her back on the mountain of work with radium that was still to be done, but not Marie Curie.

When she had recovered from the shock of Pierre's death, she moved with her two children and Pierre's father into less expensive living quarters and obtained her late husband's teaching position so that she could support her family. And she continued alone the work on radium research that she and he had been doing together.

For the next twenty-eight years she devoted all her energies to the mysteries of radium. Her work gained her fame all over the world, and a long list of high honors, medals, decorations and honorary titles were bestowed upon her from every corner of the globe. Two of them were the Nobel Prize for Physics and the Nobel Prize for Chemistry.

Finally, on Friday, July 6, 1934, death came to Marie Curie, probably as a result of her work with the powerful new element she had discovered. She was buried alongside her husband, Pierre, in the cemetery at Sceaux, France. She is still regarded as the greatest woman physicist the world has ever known.

4

The Little Animals

ANTON VAN LEEUWENHOEK
(1632–1723)

Down through the centuries great medical discoveries have been made by highly trained and dedicated men, doctors, surgeons and chemists diligently seeking the solution to one or more thoroughly baffling problems. In some cases, success was finally attained only after long, painstaking, step-by-step effort, interlaced with galling frustration, heartbreaking setbacks and bitter disappointment. In other cases, a bit of heaven-sent, pure luck suddenly opened a sealed door to the answer the scientist had been seeking.

In one or two rare instances a great medical discovery was made by someone who was not faced with any baffling problem at all, and so wasn't even seeking a solution—someone who was neither doctor, surgeon, nor chemist, and probably wouldn't have been able to tell the difference between a mild case of mumps and a fractured tibia—and yet who was to help protect the health of all generations to follow.

Such is the story of Anton van Leeuwenhoek, born in Delft, Holland, in 1632.

As a boy in school Leeuwenhoek was considerably less than a brilliant student; in fact, he was far below average in his class. He did possess a terrific curiosity, and a dogged persistency in appeasing that curiosity, whenever anything interested him. The trouble was that only very rarely did anything really interest Leeuwenhoek. At fifteen he tired of school, probably to the great relief of his frustrated teachers, and went to Amsterdam, where he got a job as a clerk in a dry goods shop. By the time he was twenty or so, he had saved up a little money and had also become tired of his job. So he went back to Delft and set himself up in his own dry goods business.

For a number of years Leeuwenhoek operated his little store in Delft and managed to make a halfway decent living. During this time, he married twice and became the father of four or five children. Eventually, though, he tired of his own business as well, and took a job as janitor at the Delft City Hall. By this time he had pretty well demonstrated to his friends and acquaintances that he was no ball of fire at anything. He was just a rather religious, honest, and somewhat ignorant man, who eventually tired of whatever he was doing and switched to something else, and he would probably go on being just as he was until the day he died.

Perhaps that is the way it would have been had not a friend stopped by to visit with Anton van Leeuwenhoek one day.

His friend showed him a piece of plain glass that had been ground into a lens, and when Leeuwenhoek looked through it at the end of his finger, he was astonished to see that it made his finger twice normal size. He was instantly fascinated, and bursting with curiosity. He asked his friend where he had got the lens and was told that it had been bought in one of the Delft shops. His friend told him the price he had paid, and although it was not very much, it was one hundred per cent too much as far as Anton van Leeuwenhoek was concerned.

His curiosity was now running wild, and he was determined to do anything to appease that curiosity by obtaining a lens of his own, so that he, too, could peer through it and see things twice their normal size. Anything, that is, with the exception of paying any of his own hard-earned money. That he would not do, for he was that kind of a man.

"I will not buy one of these things," he told his friend. "I will make one of my own."

"You will *what?*" his friend gasped in utter astonishment. "Anton, you don't know what you are talking about. Why it takes a trained craftsman with years of experience to grind a lens such as this one!"

The bullheaded stubbornness in Leeuwenhoek showed itself in the tight set of his lips.

"Nevertheless I will make my own," he said. "I will

find out how it is done and then do it myself. I may even make several of these things."

Leeuwenhoek's friend shrugged, but did not argue, for he knew it would be just a waste of breath. He, and many others, too, had for a long time suspected that Anton van Leeuwenhoek was just a little bit "tetched in the head," and that to reason with him was to reason with a brainless mule. So he shrugged and presently changed the subject.

However, slightly touched or not, Leeuwenhoek did set himself to the task of finding out how lenses were made so that he could make one of his own. During the next few years he spent every minute of his spare time haunting every establishment in the city of Delft that had anything at all to do with the making, grinding and polishing of lenses. With his great curiosity constantly after him, he found out every single thing there was to find out. He learned how to make glass, how to mold it, how much or how little to grind it, what were the best things to use as a polish, and even how to make the gold and copper rims to hold lenses in place.

And when he had obtained all that knowledge he started to make his own lenses. He made many mistakes and ruined many lenses when they'd hardly begun to take shape. He burned his hands over his smelting fire, cut his fingers and got countless blisters. But he kept at it and at it, because his driving curiosity just simply wouldn't let him quit. He just had to make a lens of his own so that he could examine all kinds of things and see what they looked like twice their normal size. A man with good eyes could see a lot, but a man with good eyes and the help of a magnifying lens would see much, much more.

As he slaved away in his little shop, seemingly going backwards as much as he went forwards, Leeuwenhoek's friends became certain that he was a crazy man. Harmless, of course, but definitely crazy just the same. But what his friends thought didn't bother Leeuwenhoek in the slightest. As a matter of fact, he never had cared a rap about the opinions of his fellow men, and he cared less for them now as he struggled day and night to be able to quench his unquenchable curiosity.

Eventually Leeuwenhoek succeeded in making a lens that suited him, at least for the moment. With it he could magnify the lines in his hands, the veins in a flower petal, and countless other things. But not magnify them nearly enough to satisfy his curiosity. There was much more to be seen, and he was curious to see it.

And now there was another urge driving him on—the urge not only to make and grind good lenses, but to make them the finest in all Holland, and to make them so small and yet so powerful that they would show him everything about even the tiniest things on the face of the earth. He would look at objects through his home-made lenses and see things no other man had ever seen before!

The question "What then?" did not matter. In fact, it never occurred to him. He wasn't seeking anything useful. All he wanted was to be able to see what was there. It didn't bother him that now his good wife was pleading with him to give up his crazy business—nor that his friends and acquaintances were visiting him less and less. They could think and do as they pleased, it was all the same to him. And as far as his wife and family were concerned, so long as he kept food on the table and a good roof over their heads they had no cause for complaint at all.

So he went on making his lenses. Not one or two, or six, or perhaps a dozen. He made hundreds of them, and spent hours over each new one, always striving to make it even more perfect than the one before. And he also started making homemade devices for focusing them, of varying designs, and fitted them with his lenses. The shelves on the walls of his shop were lined with them, each of a different design and each fitted with a slightly different-sized lens.

In a sense he became a hermit in his little workshop, when he wasn't doing his janitor's job of work at the city hall. Perhaps it is because of that, and because people considered him harmlessly crazy, that he never sold any of his lenses or lens focusers. It is quite possible that making money from his labors never even occurred to him, because he kept every single one of his lenses and *microscopes* (as they came to be called) for his own exclusive use right up to the day of his death at the age of ninety-one!

The more he studied minute things under the lens of one of his microscopes the more excited and curious he became. He had to see more and more, and the smaller the object he was able to magnify, so that his eyes could study it, the more excited he became. At first, oddly enough, he refused to believe what he saw, and was sure it was simply his imagination playing him tricks. All of his life he had been accustomed to just simple things—nothing of a complicated nature. A leaf had been a leaf, green in summer and turning to yellow and brown before it fell to the ground to decompose into nothing. And a fly had wings and a body and legs, and two big things that were its eyes, and so forth.

Everything for Anton van Leeuwenhoek had been quite simple and uncomplicated, until he started making lenses of such magnifying power that he was able to see the billions of little hairs on a fly's leg, the delicate texture of a bit of his own skin, and the intricate formations of a cross section of a tiny seed. He simply could not believe that anything so small could be made up of so many different parts.

One day in the early stages of his microscopic study of things invisible to the naked eye, he placed the single hair of a beaver under his lens and peered at it for several moments. Then he straightened up and gave an angry, disbelieving shake of his head. "Can't be!" he snorted. "I am tired and my eyes are playing me tricks."

For a moment he stood there glaring down at his microscope, and then he shouted for his wife. Fearing that harm had come to him, his wife came hurrying breathlessly into the little workshop.

"Go look!" he ordered and waved his hand.

"Look at what, Anton?" his wife wanted to know.

"That lens there, of course!" he snapped, and jabbed

a horny thumb at the instrument. "Look and tell me what you see."

Dutifully his wife went over to bend her head down and take a look. When she looked at him again there was hardly any expression on her face.

"That little string of pale-colored beads looks very pretty," she said.

Leeuwenhoek glared at her for a moment, because that was exactly the way the magnified beaver's hair had looked to him. The cell formations of the hair and the tiny connecting fibers looked like a minute string of many pale-colored beads.

"Yes, very pretty," he finally grunted, and waved his wife out of the workshop.

After that Leeuwenhoek ceased belittling his eyesight and damning his imagination. He began accepting what he saw under his lenses as actually being there—at least, to a certain extent. Because he had fallen into the habit of having only himself for company for long hours at a time, because he knew full well what his friends and neighbors thought of him, and because he was seeing things that were almost beyond the imagination, he had become one of the most suspicious and untrusting men in all Holland. So for these and other reasons, he still refused to accept for fact something his own eyes saw through his lenses for the first time.

Instead, he would leave whatever it was in place under the lens and put that particular microscope on one of the wall shelves. Then when he had ten or twenty on the shelf he would take them down one at a time after a week or so and take a second good look through the lens. And a good, studying look for Leeuwenhoek was often as long as two or three hours!

This method of satisfying his suspicious nature not only accomplished its purpose, but it also acted as an additional stimulant for his terrific sense of curiosity. On second examination not only did he see all that he had seen the first time, but many other things that his probing eyes had missed that first time. So back to the shelf went each microscope to be taken down later for a third look, and a fourth, and a fifth, and so on. Though the people of Delft thought him touched in the head, had they come around to spend many of those long hours in the workshop with him they would probably have at least admitted that Anton van Leeuwenhoek was certainly a man who didn't miss a trick if he could help it.

Another thing about Leeuwenhoek that can probably be attributed to his acquired suspicious and trustless nature is that for a long time he did not write down a single note or make a single drawing of the thousands of things he examined through his lenses. And even when he eventually did start making notes and drawings, he would not make them until he was dead certain there wasn't a single thing else to be seen in what was under the lens at the time. How amazed would Leeuwenhoek's elementary school teachers have been at the almost un-believable patience and calculating, scientific exactness of their once dull-witted pupil!

One day a man Leeuwenhoek had never seen before came to visit him at his workshop.

"My name is Regnier de Graaf," the stranger said. "I

live here in Delft, and I would like to talk with you."

Leeuwenhoek's eyes instantly darkened with suspicion. "Why?" he demanded flatly.

De Graaf smiled and made a soothing gesture with his hands. "I have heard of the lenses you grind, and the devices you make," he said quietly. "And of how you can magnify the tiniest of things many times."

Leeuwenhoek's suspicion increased and he gave his smiling visitor a baleful stare.

"I can imagine what you have heard!" he presently snorted. "Everybody thinks I am crazy. A madman who wastes his time playing with a lot of silly and senseless toys he has made. That is what you have heard about me!"

De Graaf kept smiling and shook his head. "What I have heard interests me greatly," he said evenly. "And I assure you not for the reasons you have just mentioned. Quite the contrary."

"Then why are you interested?" Leeuwenhoek challenged.

"I am a man of science," De Graaf told him, "so naturally many things interest me. And what you are doing interests me a great deal."

The dark suspicion in Leeuwenhoek's eyes abated, but not to any great extent. "It does, eh?" he grunted. "Well, what do you want?"

"I would like you to permit me to look in your microscopes at some of the objects you have been examining," De Graaf said.

Leeuwenhoek did not like that. Only his wife and his

oldest daughter, Maria, had ever looked through his microscopes at his tiny objects. Perhaps this was some kind of a trick. Perhaps this De Graaf, or whatever his name really was, was one of some jokesters who wished to have a good laugh at his expense. And yet . . .

"You'll have to give me a good reason," he finally said.

"I have already given it to you," De Graaf said quietly. "I am a man of science and what you are doing is of tremendous interest to me. I am a man of medical science, to be exact, and I happen to be a Dutch member of the Royal Society of England. Now will you please let me look through one of your microscopes?"

Something about De Graaf suddenly appealed to Leeuwenhoek and he hesitated only a moment or two longer. "Very well," he grunted, and waved at four or five microscopes on his work table. "Help yourself."

De Graaf thanked him and went over and helped himself. He looked through each lens at whatever Leeuwenhoek had placed under it. And the more he looked the more excited he became, for he knew that he was looking at things no other man of science had ever seen since the beginning of time.

When he could finally drag his eyes away from the microscopes he looked at Leeuwenhoek in wide-eyed admiration, and frankly told him that all that Leeuwenhoek had done put his own medical research work to shame, even though that work had won him membership in the Royal Society of England. After that, he plied Leeuwenhoek with questions and was even more amazed at the amount of highly technical knowledge of lens molding and grinding that the crusty Dutchman possessed, and at the wealth of knowledge he had gained from being able to study things others hadn't even seen yet.

"There is something I want you to do," De Graaf suddenly said. "Something that you must do."

"Must?" Leeuwenhoek echoed, scowling. "What if I don't feel like doing it?"

"It is not that kind of something," De Graaf said with an easy laugh. "All I want you to do is to write to the Royal Society in London and tell them all about these wonderful lenses you have made. And also about the amazing things you have been able to see and study."

Leeuwenhoek scowled again, and scratched his chin. "Why should I tell my secrets?" he demanded. "And anyway, what is this Royal Society? You have mentioned it two or three times. Royal Society for what? And what does it do?"

"Let me sit down and I will tell you about it," De Graaf said. And when they were both seated, he said, "It was first started in the days of Cromwell by a small group of learned men who were of the opinion that many beliefs handed down through the centuries simply were not true any more. Definite knowledge had now been acquired that absolutely disproved certain of the old beliefs, and once that knowledge could be made known to all men of science in England there would be great changes in the various fields of science. They used to meet in secret to make tests that disproved certain established theories, and they called themselves the Invisible Collegians."

"That's a strange-sounding name," Leeuwenhoek grunted when the other paused for breath. "And why did they meet in secret? Were they ashamed of themselves?"

"Not in the slightest," De Graaf said with a faint smile. "They were afraid for their lives. If word had ever reached Cromwell of the strange things they were doing, and the even stranger things they were claiming to be fact, he would have had them all sent straight to the hangman for being heretics. So they met in secret, but when Charles II became king they were able to come out of hiding, and in time the group became known as the Royal Society of England. Today they are learned men of science, eager and anxious to learn of new discoveries and developments in the various fields so that they may study them and, if they approve, have an account of them published in the Society's journal so that scientists in England and abroad may learn about whatever it is that has been discovered or improved upon."

De Graaf stopped again to take a quick breath.

"Now do you understand?" he asked. "The Society would be very much interested to hear from you all about what you are doing."

Inside, Leeuwenhoek was a little excited that important people like the Royal Society of England would like to hear about what he had done and was doing, but being the suspicious man he was, he wasn't eager to reveal his secrets to strangers in another land just because this De Graaf fellow begged him to.

"Well, I'll think about it," was what he eventually said. And that's the way the matter stood when De Graaf finally took his leave.

Anton van Leeuwenhoek did not write to the Royal Society on his own. However, Regnier de Graaf had rightly guessed that Leeuwenhoek wouldn't, so he wrote to the Society himself. He described as best he could all that he had seen in the workshop and strongly urged that the Society write to Leeuwenhoek officially and invite him to tell them about his wonderful work and accomplishments.

When Leeuwenhoek received that impressive letter all his brooding suspicions took a temporary holiday. He immediately sat down and wrote the Society a letter that was pages and pages long. Because of his limited amount of schooling he wasn't much of a letter writer. Also, when it came to writing a letter he was far from being the single-purpose type of person he was when perfecting his little lenses. He virtually wrote a book about himself, his life since a boy, his neighbors and others in Delft, what he thought of this and what he thought about that, and in between he gave the Society snatches of what it wanted to read.

The governing members of the Royal Society of England had to smile at the rambling letter they received from the Dutchman, but they were very much interested in the snatches of information Leeuwenhoek gave them about his work. However, there was one thing about Leeuwenhoek's work of which no mention was made in his letter. That was how he made his microscopes. Of course, the microscope as it is known today was completely unknown in Leeuwenhoek's time. The instruments he made were little more than hand frames that held his highly perfected lenses over a little glass shelf or a needle point on which the object he wanted to magnify in size was placed. Just the same, Leeuwenhoek's so-called microscope was something entirely new to the Royal Society, and so were the types of lenses that permitted him to view clearly such incredibly small objects. And that interested them perhaps more than his written descriptions of the astounding things he had been able to see and study.

So the head of the Royal Society wrote a letter back to Leeuwenhoek thanking him for his most informative letter and congratulating him for his fine work. The letter also invited Leeuwenhoek to write again to the Society telling more about his work, *and in particular* how he made his lenses and microscopes.

Unfortunately for the Royal Society, Anton van Leeuwenhoek refused point blank to do any such thing. Reveal his secrets? No, not even to such an august group of men as the Royal Society of England. Upon receipt of that second letter from the Royal Society, Leeuwenhoek began what might be appropriately called a writing marathon. For years and years afterward he virtually flooded the Society with his long-winded, a-little-of-this-and-a-little-of-that letters. He wrote and wrote and wrote about all the new invisible wonders he was able to see with his microscopes, but never once did he divulge a single word as to how he made them.

As a matter of fact, at one point the Royal Society even sent one of its members to see Leeuwenhoek and offer him a very fancy price for just one of his now hundreds of microscopes. But the suspicious Dutchman flatly refused. He was perfectly willing to supply the Royal Society with a wealth of information about the countless things he saw and studied in his invisible world, but he would not reveal any of his design and manufacturing secrets for love or money. So eventually the Society gave up trying, but they continued to welcome Leeuwenhoek's long letters about his worlds of things invisible to the naked eye.

As the years rolled on Leeuwenhoek's driving sense of curiosity increased rather than abated. He became almost a maniac at hunting out new things to peer at and study through his lenses. And one day, for no other reason than that the idea of it suddenly popped into his head, he decided to see what a little drop of rain water looked like.

Using a needle-thin glass tube he had made and shaped with his own hands he drew off a minute drop of water out of a rain barrel. Then, carefully placing it under the lens of one of his microscopes, he bent his head and took a good look. At first he didn't see anything, but after a minor adjustment or two of the lens he suddenly saw something that completely dumbfounded him. Rather, it was *things* that he saw through the lens—thousands of little living things, swimming, scrambling, and even whirling about in that minute drop of rain water.

"They are alive!" he shouted aloud. "Thousands and thousands of little animals. *Alive!*"

Utterly fascinated and enthralled, he watched the little creatures play and cavort about like so many young lambs in a sun-flooded meadow. Only, of course, they didn't look like lambs. As a matter of fact, they didn't look like anything Leeuwenhoek had ever seen before. They were all shapes and sizes. Some long and slender, some short and plump, some such tiny dots he could hardly make them out, and some so closely packed together they looked like one solid mass.

But they were all so many little animals to Leeuwenhoek, and so he gave them the name of *animalculae*. What they could actually be he couldn't even begin to guess. Of course, over a hundred and fifty years after Leeuwenhoek's death they were to become known as germs and microbes, but in his day the words germ and microbe were no part of any language on the face of the earth. So, of course, he couldn't guess or even imagine what they actually were, but he could ponder on where they came from.

Were they things God had created, just as He had created all else in the world, and had they fallen down from Heaven in the drops of rain? Or were they things that lived in the wood of the rain barrel, or things that lived on the ground and had crawled up and into the rain barrel? There was only one way to answer those questions, and so Leeuwenhoek excitedly went to work.

[77]

As a matter of fact, it was actually two steps he took to get his answers. First he took a small glass and thoroughly cleaned it with soap and hot water. Then he held the glass under the opening in the eaves of his house where the roof rain water drained off into the water barrel below. Then using his thin glass tube he drew off a minute drop of it and put it under his lens. One look, and he was able to see more thousands of his wiggling little animals. That told him that at least they did not live only in the ground. He had seen them in rain water that dripped off the roof.

Again he washed the glass clean, and although he naturally didn't so much as dream of what he was doing at the time, he actually killed all life in that glass by the process of what is now known as *sterilization*. Anyway, he went out into his yard and put his glass on the top of a post so that the falling rain couldn't possibly splash anything such as mud and bits of vegetation into the glass. And when there was enough pure rain water in the glass he drew some off and put it under his lens. One look this time and he got the answers to his questions.

His little creatures were not Heaven-sent in the rain, for he could not see a single one in that minute drop of pure rain water. So the little *animalcules* lived on the roof, in the eaves, in the wood of the rain barrel, on the ground, and perhaps everywhere. He proved himself correct by leaving the glassful of pure rain water right where it was for a few days, and then drawing some off for microscopic examination. Tiny wigglers by the thousands were swimming and whirling about in it—and so they were on the roof, on the ground, and in the very air. Everywhere!

That night Leeuwenhoek sat down and wrote another of his long letters to the Royal Society of England. He wrote of how quite by chance he had discovered the existence of minute bits of life in a minute drop of drained-off rain water. And he also wrote about the experiments he had made to prove that there were whole menageries of his little animals all about, and that they did not come down to earth from the Creator in Heaven in rain drops.

The august members of the Royal Society of England just couldn't believe the contents of that letter from Leeuwenhoek. The poor Dutchman's brain must have finally become unbalanced after long years of intensive peering through his microscopes at Heaven knew how many thousands of different things. Other letters he had written about the things he saw in his invisible world they had been inclined to believe, but thousands of little wiggling and squirming and whirling animals all about on earth and in the air? That was just too much to believe. It was just too fantastic to be given even an instant's serious consideration.

However, the learned members of the Royal Society were not so stupid as to write back to Leeuwenhoek what they actually thought about the contents of his latest letter. On the contrary, they thanked Leeuwenhoek for the information on his latest discovery, but said that it was so astounding that perhaps he would be

kind enough to tell the Society how he made his microscopes so that the Society might make one and thus be
able to confirm the amazing claims he had made.

It was a good try by the Society, but it didn't work!
Leeuwenhoek sent the Society reams more about his
animalcules, but not one word on how to make one of
his microscopes. His secrets were his secrets, and that
was all there was to it.

A few years after his discovery of the little creatures,
Anton van Leeuwenhoek made another discovery, also
by chance, that amazed him almost as much as the first.
And it had to do with a tiny single grain of pepper.
Curious as to why pepper stung the tongue he attempted
to see what was in it by putting a grain under his microscope lens. But even a single grain of pepper was too
big for his lens to magnify it to the size he wished for
study. So he soaked the grain in a drop of his pure rain
water and then with a needle point mashed it up. Then
he put a minute drop of the mashed-up pepper grain and
pure rain water under the lens of his microscope.

To his great surprise he saw swarms and swarms of
his little creatures swimming in his mixture of pepper
and rain water. And then, after hours of studying them,
he saw to his even greater surprise that the little animals
grew and multiplied their number again and again!
In short, pepper water was a wonderful breeding ground
for *animalcules.*

He repeated that experiment several times, and then
wrote all about it to the Royal Society. Its learned members were really stunned this time. They flatly refused

to believe. But since Leeuwenhoek had been right in what he claimed so many times before, the Society just had to do something about this latest claim. And the only thing they could do about it that would mean anything was to have some of their skilled members make the best microscope they possibly could.

A fairly good microscope was made, though nothing to be compared with Leeuwenhoek's. Then finally came the day when the learned men of science in England mixed pure rain water with a mashed-up pepper grain and looked at it through the microscope lens. It was true! Anton van Leeuwenhoek was far from crazy. His tiny wonders actually did exist, and what's more they grew and multiplied in pepper water! Convinced of the truth, the Society did honor to Anton van Leeuwenhoek by unanimously voting him a Fellow of the Society. That honor filled Leeuwenhoek's cup of joy to the brim, and it also served to double his output of long rambling letters to the Society from that day until the day he died.

Leeuwenhoek died in 1723, and it was only a few years before his death that he finally was forced by failing eyesight to give up his relentless probing of the invisible worlds revealed to his eye under his microscope lens. A hundred and fifty or so years later highly skilled men of science were to identify those minute bits of life as germs and microbes, give them names, and determine which types would kill or benefit other living things. But it was Anton van Leeuwenhoek, a crusty, suspicious and curious Dutchman, who saw them first.

[81]

5

The Red Death

EDWARD JENNER
(1749–1823)

The year was 1772 and the place was St. George's Hospital in London, England. It was a September morning and two men were walking along a corridor leading to the ward where hopeless cases were confined.

One of the men was Dr. John Hunter, a surgeon at St. George's and one of the most brilliant and honored men of his profession. He was a tall man in his middle sixties, with a lean face, snow-white hair, and deep-set gray eyes which could as quickly flash with anger as they could twinkle with amusement.

The other man was Edward Jenner, who was only

twenty-three years old and a complete opposite in appearance to the learned surgeon. He had heavily lidded eyes, an extremely large nose, and unruly straw-colored hair. He was also quite thick-set, and something less than average in height. He had been the last of six children, born May 17, 1749, to the Reverend and Mrs. Stephen Jenner at the vicarage in the Valley of Berkely, Gloucestershire.

At the age of fourteen, he began his study of pharmacy and medicine under Dr. Daniel Ludlow, of Sodbury, near Bristol. Seven years later, Dr. Ludlow arranged for him to go to London to serve a two-year "house student" apprenticeship under the guidance of the famed Dr. Hunter. During those two years, young Jenner proved to be such a brilliant student that Dr. Hunter strongly urged him to remain in London and set up his own practice. He painted a very glowing picture of fame and fortune for Jenner in London, but the young doctor was not to be tempted, even though he had become very fond of the learned surgeon and would have liked to please him by staying.

The goal he sought for himself was not to be found in London. It was in the Valley of Berkely, or the Vale, as it was called. His roots were there in the beautiful, rolling, green countryside, with its warm sunshine and clean, fresh air. He had not liked London at all. The constant noise and the seemingly ever-hanging pall of soot smoke that fairly plugged up the lungs had repelled him since the very first day of his stay. He wanted only to return to his beloved Vale and devote the rest of his life to tending the sick and the injured who lived on the soil of his birthplace.

In a few days he would return to the Vale, but at the moment he was accompanying his dear friend and medical mentor on his morning hospital rounds.

When they reached the door of the ward for the hopeless cases, Dr. Hunter paused a moment, as if steeling himself for what was inside, and then opened the door and entered. He walked with Jenner over to a bed where lay a little boy of eight years, but who would not live to see his ninth birthday. He had shortly before been a fine-looking, healthy lad, but now his whole body was covered with ugly, flaming sores.

Dr. Hunter touched his hand gently to the fevered brow, peered down into the puffed and pain-filled eyes, and sighed softly.

"You recognize the symptoms, of course, Jenner?" he murmured without taking his eyes from the doomed boy.

"Of course," Edward Jenner replied quickly. "Smallpox. The cursed Red Death." He paused a moment and then asked the question, though knowing full well what the answer would be. "Is there no hope, Dr. Hunter?"

The older man slowly shook his head. "None at all," he said heavily. "All we can do is to try and make him as comfortable as possible until the good Lord takes him."

Jenner groaned and clenched his fists in helpless frustration. "There must be some way!" he exclaimed, as though to himself. "There must be some way to rid the world of this terrible thing!"

[85]

Dr. Hunter shrugged and raised his hands slightly, palms upward. "Perhaps one day someone will discover a way," he murmured. "Until then, God help the millions who are doomed to contract the dreaded disease."

Edward Jenner nodded grimly. The learned surgeon's use of the word "millions" had been no exaggeration. Millions had already succumbed to the terrible Red Death since it first reached Europe, by way of Asia and Africa, in the tenth century.

The great city of London, where he now was, had been first struck in 1628, and over fourteen hundred men, women, and children had died from smallpox in each succeeding year. In the year of 1752 a record total of thirty-five hundred Londoners alone had died from the Red Death. And the terrible disease struck down the highborn as well as the lowborn, for in 1628 Queen Mary II of England had died of smallpox.

In a period of a hundred years twenty million Europeans had succumbed to smallpox, and during those years it swept across the ocean to the New World where millions more were struck down and died. When the Spaniards conquered Mexico they brought smallpox to that little land, and in the short space of three years as many millions of Mexican Indians fell ill with it and died. And it was recorded in medical journals the young Jenner had read that in 1721 a single smallpox-afflicted sailor from a British ship that put into the port of Boston, in the American Colonies, had started an epidemic in that city that took over six thousand lives before it had run its course.

[86]

THE RED DEATH

Smallpox! The Red Death that struck without warning, and then just as suddenly disappeared, to wait and strike again elsewhere. In Jenner's world of medicine there was no cure for it, and only a method of prevention that was a matter of blind luck, and nothing else. It had come from Turkey and was an inoculation process called "engrafting." It was simply a process of inoculating a healthy person with real smallpox venom in the hope that by inducing a mild case of the disease the person would become immune from it for the rest of his life. Unfortunately, though, far more persons who were engrafted contracted a severe case of smallpox and died than contracted a mild case and become immune.

Shaking his head, as if to drive away the ugly thoughts, young Jenner hesitated, and then asked a question. "Do you know what cowpox is, sir?"

Dr. Hunter put a hand to his mouth to hide an amused smile, and presently nodded gravely.

"Why, yes, I believe I do," he said quietly. "It is a very contagious disease among cows. Inflamed and crusty sores appear on their udders, and anyone milking the cow becomes infected with the disease. But not with serious results. Painful sores appear on the milkers' hands and wrists, and they suffer spells of high fever and nausea. In a few days, though, the sores disappear and the milkers become quite well again."

The learned surgeon paused and regarded Jenner with a half amused and half quizzical eye. "What made you ask that?" he wanted to know.

Younger Jenner hesitated again and even started to shrug off the question, but changed his mind. "There is a belief in the valley where I was born, sir," he replied slowly, "that anyone who gets the cowpox cannot get the smallpox."

Dr. Hunter started to snort, but stopped it and gave a little impatient gesture with one hand. "You believe that?" he demanded. "You have perhaps seen sufficient evidence to prove that it is true?"

Edward Jenner flushed slightly and took a moment or two before he spoke. "I neither believe it nor disbelieve it, sir," he said finally. "But I have often heard it said by people in the Vale that the number of milkers who had the cowpox and did not get the smallpox was greater than the number of those who had the cowpox and also got the smallpox. I—I am just wondering . . ." He let the rest die away and shrugged silently.

"What are you wondering, Jenner?" Dr. Hunter prompted, his gray eyes now fixed seriously on the younger man.

"If cowpox isn't something to do some thinking about," Jenner said with a frown. "I will have plenty of chance to study it, and perhaps even test the truth of the legend. And—" He stopped and smiled in embarrassment. "At least it's a thought, sir," he said a little doggedly.

Dr. Hunter nodded soberly, and impulsively reached out a hand to grip the younger man's shoulder. "It is indeed," he said quietly. "Everything we have in medicine today began with a man's thought. Perhaps this thought you have will one day produce a miracle for the world. But right now let us resume our rounds."

"Yes, sir," Jenner murmured. But as he dropped into step with the older man a great dream was burgeoning in his mind. A dream that he would spend almost his entire life in fulfilling.

Some five days later Edward Jenner said good-bye to his dear friend and teacher in London and returned to his native Berkely. As his father and mother had died when he was a young boy, and four of his sisters and brothers had married and moved away, there was only his oldest brother, Stephen Jr., living in the old family home. Their reunion was of the happiest, for they had always been exceptionally close to each other, despite the fact that Stephen was seventeen years older.

For the first week or so, young Jenner spent almost every waking hour riding his horse about the Vale, meeting old friends again, and, as he described it, getting the stench of London out of his nose and lungs. Stephen often rode with him and listened with great interest to the young doctor's tales of his two years in London. And when Edward almost shyly told him of his great dream of finding some way to rid the world of the terrible Red Death, he did not scoff or laugh as others might have done on hearing such big words from young lips. He knew nothing of medicine, but he deeply loved his younger brother and had complete faith in him. And so he quickly encouraged the new doctor to hold fast to his great dream and exert every effort to make it come true.

Unfortunately, though, it was not possible for Edward Jenner to set to work immediately on solving the problem that had baffled the entire medical world since the beginning of time. For one thing, his first concern was to establish a medical practice in the Vale so that he could earn a living. And for another thing, there was no epidemic of cowpox present in the valley at that time. Cowpox, like the dreaded smallpox, was something that struck lightning-swift, out of nowhere, and just as swiftly disappeared, not to strike again for sometimes as long as four or five years.

When he could begin working toward his great dream it was his intention to *inoculate* deliberately with cowpox matter (discharge from a sore, or pus) to protect the body against smallpox if possible, and to try to determine whether it was the cowpox matter or something else that caused inoculations to fail in that purpose.

However, first things first. For five years his great dream remained only a dream, but during that time he built up a fine practice in the Vale and became one of its best-liked and respected doctors. Then in 1778, both cowpox and smallpox struck the valley and he was finally able to begin a struggle which was to last for many bitter and disheartening years before victory was within his grasp.

For those who were struck down by the dreaded Red Death, he could do no more than Dr. Hunter had been able to do for the doomed little boy in St. George's Hospital. But, in a reverse sort of way, the doomed ones were able to do something for him. They made it possible for him to obtain smallpox "venom" and use it to inoculate all the healthy ones who came to him, in order to create an induced, mild case of the disease, and *perhaps* make them immune from the Red Death.

Three of the many who came to him had come down with cowpox, and not believing in the old legend, they had come to him to get the induced smallpox inoculation just to play safe. And so those three became Jenner's first "guinea pigs" in his long fight against the Red Death. He inoculated them with smallpox matter to induce a mild case of the disease, and waited eagerly for the eighth and crucial day. When it arrived not one of the three milkers had fallen sick with an induced mild case of smallpox. None showed any ill effects whatsoever!

To make sure he had followed the correct inoculating procedure, Jenner inoculated the three milkers a second time, and waited another eight days. At the end of those eight days the milkers still showed no signs of induced smallpox, but Jenner still wasn't satisfied. He inoculated them a third time, but once again the results were the same. The trio remained in perfect health. They were definitely immune from smallpox.

For Jenner it was a victory, but one so small it almost couldn't be called such. True, in three separate cases he had proved the old legend of the Vale to be true, but he had failed to find any kind of an answer to the still all-important question. Why did cowpox make some immune from smallpox, but not others?

Was there something other than cowpox that made one immune? Did a person's state of health at the time he had cowpox make the difference in his not contracting smallpox? Was cowpox effective against smallpox for only a certain length of time?

Those and many other unanswered questions plagued Edward Jenner day and night. More determined than ever to ferret out the answers, he toured the length and breadth of the Vale. He talked with those who had contracted cowpox in the past, and those who had contracted it only recently. He made all kinds of notes to be studied and carefully analyzed later, but because he spent so much time roaming about the Vale his own private practice began to fall off.

Oddly enough, though, it actually wasn't his being away from his home for such long periods of time that caused his practice to slacken. Rather, it was the impression he gave those to whom he talked during his tour seeking knowledge. At first the dairymen cooperated with him completely, because they thought he was trying to stamp out cowpox. But when he corrected that impression by telling them that it was smallpox and not cowpox he hoped to stamp out, the dairymen became very angry.

True, some who had lost dear ones to the dreaded Red Death saw a ray of hope in his work and prayed for his success. The vast majority, however, reacted as would people out of the Dark Ages. Superstition-filled minds regarded him as a sinful man going against God's will. In short, if God had not meant for man to get smallpox

THE RED DEATH

He would not have put it here on earth. Therefore Edward Jenner was defying God in seeking to rid the earth of what the Almighty had put there!

Some people, the better-educated ones, did not look upon him as a sinful man defying God's will, but simply as a plain fool wasting his time seeking the end of a rainbow that just did not exist. They claimed the Vale legend to be no more than a silly rumor, and they cited countless cases to prove it was exactly that.

The reaction to his efforts shocked Jenner and hurt him deeply, but it did not in the slightest lessen his determination to attain his goal—not even when the members of a medical club in the Vale to which he belonged poked holes in his belief and urged him to forget his will-o'-the-wisp quest and devote his time exclusively to medical and surgical practice; not even when people started calling him a crazy crank, began to shun him, and make him feel unwelcome in their homes. Many a night he returned to his home a heartsick and frustrated man, but by the next morning's light his great dream was as bright as ever.

For the next four years he applied himself to the task of following his dream whenever he could spare the time from his practice. One thing in particular he did was to examine every bovine and human victim of cowpox possible and make an intensive study of the symptoms of the disease. He noted that the pustules (sores) on the udders of a cow were a dull blue in color, and that the pustules on the hands and wrists of the milkers became inflamed blisters that were filled with a yellowish matter.

Also, the milkers experienced attacks of chills and high fever. They suffered violent head and body pains, and had spells of delirium for the first three or four days.

Then in 1782 a great truth suddenly dawned on him, and in theory he was able to take a long step toward achieving his life's purpose.

It came as a result of a diligent study and analysis of the copious notes he had made during his travels up and down the Vale. He realized that he had allowed the cowpox symptoms of both the cow and the milker to trick him. Actually, they were not always the same in appearance. In fact, they varied greatly. In some cases the pustules on the cow's udder were a dull blue, but sometimes a different shade of blue. Sometimes they were round in shape, but sometimes quite irregular. In some cases, the pustules were almost bursting with yellowish matter, but in some cases there was hardly any of the yellowish matter at all. And, most confusing of all, in some cases the pustules disappeared in a few days, but in others not for weeks. In short, there was no constant similarity in the appearance of the symptoms of a cow struck with cowpox.

The same thing was also true as regards a milker infected with cowpox. Usually pustules appeared on the hands and wrists, and there was a swelling at the armpits, but not always. Normally, a day or so after coming down with cowpox, the milker suffered head and body pains, and spells of vomiting and delirium, but among Jenner's notes were some cases where the victim suffered none of those things. And although he had case notes showing that the patient recovered in four or five days, he also had case notes showing that three and four times that length of time had been necessary for complete recovery.

The answer to the riddle, when it struck like lightning, was obvious. Jenner was stunned he had not realized it long before. It was simply that what was being called cowpox *was actually more than one disease.* It was, he now firmly believed, several diseases, any one of which could infect a milker's hands and wrists. And because all the symptoms were so much alike, the various diseases had been given but one name, cowpox!

Convinced that he had found a key to the mystery of why some milkers with cowpox became immune from smallpox while others did not, Jenner then began the task of determining which of the several diseases lumped under the one name was the true cowpox.

However, it was not a task he could accomplish in a matter of weeks, or even months. One reason was because cowpox in the Vale chose that moment to make another one of its sudden disappearances and remain away for three years. And another reason was the press of his now fast-mounting medical practice. Even though many in the Vale still considered him a crazy crank as far as his dream was concerned, they were forced to admit that he was a very skilled doctor, and so they came to him from all over with their ills.

During the five years that passed before he was finally able to determine and isolate the true cowpox, he married Catherine Kingscote. She quickly took an active interest in the fulfillment of his great dream, and proved to be a constant source of comfort and new strength when defeat and even complete failure were to stare him in the face.

Edward Jenner found out that a cow infected with true cowpox had pustules of irregular shape on her udders. They were a definite pale blue in color, and were completely ringed with inflammation. And when the cow became sick her milk supply either stopped altogether or decreased to a very small amount.

In the case of a milker infected with true cowpox, the first symptoms were inflamed spots on the hands and wrists, looking very much like small burns. However, they quickly took on the shape of round sores which then became blisters filled with yellowish matter. The victim's pulse quickened, and he had shivers and pains in the loins and limbs. There were head pains, too, and spells of delirium that lasted (usually) for no more than four days before recovery began.

Highly gratified at having at long last determined what was the true cowpox, Jenner then set about to make a series of tests to check and prove his belief. However, he had just barely gotten underway with his tests when the great dream he had been working toward for ten long years blew up in his face.

The year was 1791. Smallpox struck the Vale again, and this time dairy workers who had had Jenner's so-called true cowpox only a short time before were struck down by the real smallpox. When Jenner was told the news he was stunned, and simply could not believe it to be true. But when he made a personal investigation of his own, he was forced to accept the fact. He saw the truth for himself, and his great dream lay in ashes. All his years of work, the checking and rechecking, had not proved a thing. His firm belief that true cowpox could protect from smallpox simply wasn't true!

Jenner was so stunned and beaten down in spirit that he came very close to burying his great hope deep and forgetting it forever. His wife, though, would not let him give up in miserable failure, and when he had recovered somewhat from the crushing blow he did resolve to persevere. He went back over every step he had taken during the long ten years, checking and rechecking his notes and test records. He even sent them to some of his medical friends in the Vale to examine, in the hope that they might discover one small thing he had missed or overlooked. But no mistakes were found; there was not even one tiny factor that he had failed to take into account. The burning question was still there: Why had his true cowpox failed to make a person immune from smallpox?

For the next two years the great question hung in his brain unanswered, like a dead weight. Then in 1793 the answer came to him quite by chance.

Cowpox hit the dairy farms again that year, and Jenner had had two of the stricken cows brought to his own barn so that he could study them around the clock if he wanted to. One of the cows was in an advanced stage of cowpox, and the other had just started to show symptoms of the disease.

[97]

He maintained almost a constant watch of the two cows, and made notes on everything he observed as the disease progressed in each one. For the next few days, he completely neglected his general practice and almost went without sleep. More often than not his wife took his meals out to him in the barn. Then, very early one morning, when he was half dead for the want of sleep and chilled to the bone in the cold barn, the answer he sought suddenly came to him in the form of one word. Strength!

That was it, strength! As the cowpox pustule gains in strength, as the disease advances, so must the strength of its yellowish matter. And only when the yellowish matter was at its fullest strength could it protect against smallpox. So it meant that down through the years every man or woman infected with cowpox had contracted the disease in one of its three stages—*before* the yellowish matter in the pustule had reached its fullest strength, *when* it had reached its fullest strength, or *after* it had reached that point and was lessening in strength. Only those who had contracted the cowpox disease when the pustule's matter was at full strength had become immune from smallpox!

Chilled to the bone and dog-tired, but happier than he had been at any other moment in his life, Edward Jenner raised his eyes upward and breathed a prayer of thanks. Victory and the fulfillment of his great dream now truly seemed very close at hand. Now he possessed the knowledge to give his theory the critical test and prove that the terrible Red Death could be beaten.

He would not, however, make his critical test with the pustule matter of a cow with cowpox. He must make it with the pustule matter of a human being infected with true cowpox. He would inject it into another human being to bring about a case of induced cowpox. When the pustule matter of that second person reached its strongest point, some of it could be injected into a third person, and so on, until all in the Vale had been made immune from smallpox.

The critical test Edward Jenner planned to make would actually be a two-part test, with the second half of the test definitely deciding whether it really meant victory or miserable failure again. The first step was to produce a case of induced cowpox in a perfectly healthy person. The second part was to inoculate that same person later with smallpox to see if a case of induced smallpox resulted. If it did not, then his theory would become proven fact.

But once again, as so often had been the case during Jenner's long years of struggle, it was not possible for him to go right ahead and obtain indisputable proof of his theory. It was to take time to find someone with a case of true cowpox in its most advanced stage and the pustule matter at full strength. It would also take time to find someone who would consent to being a subject for the test. But what really held him back from making his crucial test was an epidemic of typhoid fever that struck the Vale. Because of his great hurry and desire to aid others, Jenner failed to take sufficient precautions himself and the epidemic almost took his own life.

However, in May of 1796, a woman milker came to him with a case of the true cowpox which he realized would reach its most advanced stage in three day's time. He treated the sores for the time being and asked the woman to be sure to come back in exactly three days. When she promised she would, Jenner immediately set about finding a person who had not had cowpox or smallpox, or even an induced case of smallpox.

He could not use himself, or his wife, or their young son, as all three had long since been inoculated for induced smallpox and were almost certainly immune. He had, therefore, to go outside his own family, and he thought of a twelve-year-old boy, James Phipps, who lived with his parents in a nearby cottage.

To get the parents' permission to use James for his all-important test, Jenner explained carefully what he wanted to do with James, why he wanted to do it, and exactly how he intended to do it. Also, what success would mean to the entire world. At first the parents were enraged by his suggestion and came close to ordering him out of the house. Eventually, however, he was able to convince them that the chance of failure and possible death for the boy was only one per cent. That, added to the fact that both parents had lost loved ones to the dreaded disease, and longed to see it stamped out, finally resulted in their giving Jenner their consent to make his test.

On May 14, Jenner took some of the yellowish pustule matter from one of the cowpox sores of the woman milker's hands and inoculated young James Phipps.

THE RED DEATH

Many times a day for the next few days he rode his horse over to the Phipps' cottage to observe the boy. He saw the boy fall ill, the familiar pustules start to appear, and all the other symptoms he had seen hundreds of times. But this time he was seeing something that neither he nor anyone else had ever seen before—a human being coming down with cowpox contracted from another human being.

At the end of four days James Phipps recovered from his case of induced cowpox. And on the first of July Edward Jenner conducted the second and most crucial part of the test. He inoculated James Phipps with real smallpox matter taken from a man living in the Vale who had been struck down by the dreaded Red Death just a few days before.

Then began the soul-searing wait. Jenner truly believed with all his heart that the chance of failure and danger to the boy was no more than one per cent. But there was that one per cent, and the anguish and torment he must have suffered cannot possibly be expressed in words. The wait must have been a living hell for both Jenner and the boy's parents, but when the crucial seventh and eighth days had come and gone, their prayers were answered. James Phipps did not show a single symptom of induced smallpox. Nor did he in the days that followed. The long battle was won. Edward Jenner had created a medical miracle that spelled the doom of the terrible Red Death.

It was indeed a great and wonderful victory for Edward Jenner, but for years to come it was little more than a hollow one! Incredible as it may seem, the medical world simply refused to believe his claim. To substantiate it, Jenner made twenty-one tests similar to the one he had made on young James Phipps. He wrote out a detailed report of all those tests, and of all his work and findings since his study started, and sent it to the London Royal Society for publication in that august body's journal. But that cautious and highly skeptical group sent it back to him with the suggestion that he recheck everything to find out where he had gone astray with his somewhat unfounded claims!

Jenner was angry over the Society's rebuff, and so were all his medical compatriots in the Vale. They angrily decided to take matters into their own hands, and they did. With Jenner's help they published his very detailed report, along with complete instructions on how to perform the test, and began circulating it throughout the English medical world. Jenner went up to London and practically begged some of that city's leading doctors to try the test and discover for themselves if what he claimed was true; but none would agree to do it, and he returned to the Vale more angry and baffled than before.

If that were not enough, the detailed report that was being circulated throughout the English medical world started to cause trouble. It contained detailed instructions on exactly what to do and how to do it, but some doctors who read the report gave it a try without following the directions closely. As a result more of their patients died than were made immune from smallpox,

and Edward Jenner was blamed for these stupid and un-
warranted failures. Instead of receiving acclaim for
making a great medical discovery, he was made an object of scorn and derision. For a while it looked as if
all his work had been for nothing, and that the great discovery he had made for mankind's benefit was to be
shunted aside and completely forgotten.

In the face of all the opposition, he fought on to
preserve his victory and his name, and finally he won
out. At last two famous London doctors agreed to make
the test, and in both cases it was an unqualified success.
These events started the tide turning in his favor. Over
in France, where at first the unconvinced had given his
process the humorous name of *vaccination,* which in
French meant *en-cowing,* two or three prominent French
doctors tried the test, and also met with complete success. German doctors tried it with success, and in
Vienna, Austria, the great Dr. De Carra wrote to Jenner
asking him for sufficient vaccine to inoculate every person in his country. Perhaps the most convincing touch
of all was when George III, the reigning king of England, was inoculated in St. James Palace.

And so in 1799, twenty-seven years after the birth of
his great dream, Edward Jenner finally saw the medical
world pick up its sword, as he had done, to drive the
terrible Red Death from the face of the earth. In that
year, fame came to him at last, and high honors and
awards were showered upon him from all over the
world. Of all the honors and awards he received, the
one he cherished most was a simply written letter from

the chiefs of five American Indian nations thanking and blessing him for giving them the power to drive the dreaded Red Death from their tepees.

Edward Jenner died quietly at his home in the Vale on January 25, 1823, at the age of seventy-four, but this great man's service to all the world lives forever.

6

Madness by Infection

LOUIS PASTEUR
(1822–1895)

A fine rain was beginning to fall on a spring evening in
1884 as a cab driver reined his horse to a stop in front
of a modest three-story brick building in the Quai de
Passy section of Paris. Bending down from his high seat,
he gravely accepted the five-franc fare from the man who
alighted from the cab, and then tipped his hat and
drove off.

For a moment or two Louis Pasteur, the most honored chemist and scientist in all France, if not in all
the world, stood there staring absently after the retreat-
ing cab. Then, turning slowly, he stared at the front
door of the red brick building, almost as though he

were not quite sure he had arrived at his correct destination. He was a short, stocky man, now in his sixty-second year, and he had straight black hair and a thick beard. His face was blunt-featured and he wore very thick spectacles. Slightly stoop-shouldered, he walked with a pronounced limp in his left leg, the aftermath of a mild stroke he had suffered sixteen years before.

Presently he made a little movement with his shoulders, as though shrugging aside an annoying thought, and went into his house, where his wife, Marie, to whom he had been married for thirty-five years, greeted him with a warm smile and a kiss. Helping him off with his hat and coat, she gently guided him to his favorite easy chair in their downstairs living room. He sank down into it with a sigh and almost automatically picked up the small cup of hot chocolate she always had ready and waiting for him, no matter at what hour he arrived home from his laboratory.

As they sipped their chocolate, Marie Pasteur spoke about the weather and a bit of social news she had learned that day, but suddenly she stopped and peered knowingly at the thousand-mile-away look she recognized in her famous husband's eyes.

"Tell me about it, if you like, my dear," she said softly. "You know I am always glad to listen."

Pasteur shook himself slightly, and glanced at her with a puzzled frown. "Eh? What's that, Marie?" he murmured.

"You are not here, but still in your laboratory," she

said with a little laugh. "So tell me about your newest problem. Perhaps the telling will help you."

The great tenderness he had always felt for her showed in Pasteur's dark eyes as he impulsively reached out a hand and pressed her arm. "I was not thinking of problems," he said. "But of myself. Yet perhaps that is the greatest problem I face. Myself."

For a moment Madame Pasteur watched him, frowning, and then smoothed the frown away with a teasing smile. "For me at times, perhaps yes," she said. "But never for Louis Pasteur. But what do you mean by that, anyway?"

Pasteur thoughtfully stroked his thick beard and scowled down at his empty chocolate cup. "I am a successful failure," he blurted out. "I have not done what I have wanted to do most. And time is flying by so fast."

"You're being utterly ridiculous," his wife said sharply, "not to mention completely confusing. What on earth are you talking about, Louis?"

He smiled wryly, and started to move his hand to dismiss the subject, but changed his mind. "People," he said. "I have wanted so much to help people."

His wife stared at him in amazement. "And you haven't?" she said challengingly. "Was it not Louis Pasteur who solved the problem of diseases in wines that were costing French wine makers, *people*, millions in loss every year? Was it not he who solved the problem of disease in silkworms and saved one of France's most prosperous industries? And did he not discover a vaccine to prevent anthrax in cattle that saved hundreds of French farmers, *people,* from complete ruin? And discovered a vaccine for chicken cholera that was about to wipe out the chicken industry in France? And did not this Louis Pasteur help millions of people by discovering a heating process that destroys deadly germs in wine and milk, and which has been named *Pasteurization* in his honor?"

She stopped to shake her head at the hand he was raising in mild protest. "Let me finish!" she said. "Those are a few of the things this Louis Pasteur has done for *people.* And for his great work *people* have bestowed upon him two of France's highest honors—the Grand Cross of the Legion of Honor, and election to the Académie Française, composed of France's most distinguished *people* of the arts and sciences. Louis, my dear, you must not be feeling well to talk such utter nonsense!"

Pasteur smiled gently and waited a moment or two until the faint flush of annoyance and exasperation had disappeared from her lovely face.

"You do not understand, my dear," he then said quietly. "I meant I have wanted to help people who were *sick,* but I have only helped people who had silkworms, or cows, or horses, or sheep, or chickens that were sick."

"But you are a chemist, not a doctor!" Marie Pasteur exclaimed. "Sickness in people is a medical problem."

Pasteur nodded absently, and for a brief moment he was tempted to speak of what was in his mind, but he refrained. To do so would only arouse in her heart the pain he now felt in his own. Marie had borne him five children, a son and four daughters, but only the son, Jean-Batiste, and one daughter, Marie-Louise, were now alive. The other three daughters, Jeanne, Camille and Cecile, had died at a tender age from the dreaded typhoid fever.

Each time one of his daughters had fallen ill with the disease, he had sat constantly by her bedside utterly helpless to stay the hand of death. And each time he whispered good-bye to one of them as she was lowered into her tiny grave he had sworn the solemn vow to fight disease in humans for her sweet sake, and to destroy disease as disease had destroyed her. That had been a long, long time ago, and he had not yet fulfilled the vows to his dead daughters.

"And besides," his wife's voice presently came to him, "you are doing something for the good of sick people. You are working on that terrible disease, hydrophobia. Stamping out rabies from the bite of a mad dog is certainly helping sick people. Every father and mother of children in the world will bless you forever!"

"But I haven't done it yet," Pasteur said with a sad shake of his head. "It is now exactly four years since I began studying the problem. I have made hundreds of tests and experiments on dogs infected with rabies, but I have learned hardly anything that was not already known when I started."

"Learning even a little is something," Marie Pasteur said gently.

"It has been so very little," Pasteur said heavily. "We know that rabies, the 'dumb madness' as people call it, is carried to a human being in the saliva of the mad dog that bites him. We have learned that cauterizing the bite wound sometimes prevents the disease from taking effect. And we suspect that in some people bitten by a rabid dog there is something that kills the germ and stops it from taking effect. And we know that most human victims show symptoms of rabies in two weeks, but some have remained well for months afterward!"

He suddenly stopped and ground a clenched fist into the palm of his other hand. "Why?" he spoke the word fiercely. "Why some two weeks, and others not for months? And what is the hydrophobia germ, and where do you look for it? We have looked everywhere, but not found it yet. How do you fight something you can't even see?"

As Pasteur lapsed into moody silence, his wife started to speak, but thought better of it. Instead, she remained seated quietly for a few moments. When Pasteur continued to remain enveloped by moody silence she got up from her chair and went out into the kitchen to prepare their supper.

The next morning, Pasteur got up at his usual early hour, and after a hastily eaten breakfast, went straight to his laboratory, some dozen blocks from his home. Also as usual, he found his two assistants, Emile Roux and Charles Chamberland, already there and waiting for him. The two men were not only his assistants but two of his dearest friends in the world. They had worked with him for years and had been of inestimable value to him in his past great work. As a matter of fact, when the French Government had awarded him the Grand Cross of the Legion of Honor, he had refused to accept it unless Roux and Chamberland were also decorated.

"And so today we make one more test, eh?" Roux murmured with a scowl when Pasteur joined them.

"Another test," the famed chemist said. Then with a faint smile, "But perhaps the last of this kind. I have been thinking."

"Of what?" Chamberland demanded, instantly all ears. "What have you been thinking about?"

Pasteur shrugged and picked up a thin glass tube from a nearby table.

"Something different," he said. "But first let us make this test for today."

Knowing well from long experience that it was impossible to get Louis Pasteur to speak of what was in his mind when he did not wish to, Roux and Chamberland did not press him, but forthwith set about preparing for the test.

There were several cages in the huge room, each containing a dog inflicted with rabies. The cage they went to contained a bulldog, and at their approach the animal set up a hoarse growling that filled the room. Its blood-shot eyes rolled and green foam sprayed from its jaws as it hurled itself at the bars of the cage in a rage-blinded effort to get at them. Putting on thick leather gloves, through which the mad dog's fangs could not pierce, Roux and Chamberland opened the cage door and seized the vicious animal. Holding it helpless between them, they stretched it out on a table.

While they kept the dog's head motionless, Pasteur, with a glass tube between his lips, carefully bent down and drew off some of the green saliva from its mouth. As Roux and Chamberland returned the dog to its cage, Pasteur transferred the foamy green saliva to a syringe and went over to another pen in which were half a dozen small pigs. He inoculated each of the small pigs with the green saliva in the syringe, and put the syringe back in its special holder.

"Do you expect any different results this time?" Roux asked, giving him a shrewd look.

Pasteur smiled and shook his head. "No, I do not," he said. "I am quite sure the results will be the same as they were in all the other tests. But we will not know until tomorrow, so we'll just have to wait until then. In the meantime we all have other work to do."

And that was that, as far as satisfying the curiosity of the two assistants went. Whatever else Louis Pasteur had in mind, they were not to hear about it until the pig-inoculation results were known on the morrow. So once again they held back their probing questions and applied themselves to various other duties in the laboratory.

The following morning when the three of them examined the six rabies-inoculated pigs, they saw that the results were exactly the same as many other times. All six pigs had fallen ill with hydrophobia during the night and died.

"Which tells us nothing we do not already know," Charles Chamberland commented dryly. "And that puts us right back where we were when we started."

"It is hopeless!" Roux grunted heavily. "When we can't even find the germ that causes this cursed thing, how can we possibly expect to find a cure for it? Not to mention a preventive!"

"I have been thinking," Pasteur said, as though he had not even heard the others speak. "I think we have not been able to find the hydrophobia germ because we haven't looked for it in the right place."

"Right place?" Roux echoed with a puzzled frown. "And just where is the right place we haven't looked at?"

"The brain and nervous system," Pasteur said. And as his assistants' eyes started to widen, he continued. "Why do some victims fall ill in two weeks, some not for months, and a few not at all?" he asked. "Because, I think, in different people it takes different lengths of time for the germ to travel from the bite wound to the brain, where it does its deadly work. And in a few lucky people there is something that overpowers the germ and destroys it before it can reach the brain. Perhaps a certain type of blood they have, I do not know. But something prevents the germ from reaching their brain, and so they are spared."

"I agree!" The words almost exploded from Charles Chamberland's mouth. "The brain and nervous system, of course! That explains the symptoms in both humans and animals. The fits and convulsions, the terrible thirst,

[113]

the inability to swallow, the uncontrollable working of the jaws, and the final paralysis. Of course!"

"And you, Emile?" Pasteur murmured, looking at his other assistant.

Emile Roux nodded instantly. "I also agree!" he exclaimed. Then he added, his whole face beaming, "Once again Louis Pasteur has found the answer!"

"Perhaps," the chemist said with a cautioning gesture of one hand. "We have no proof, yet. But I believe we have found a way to get that proof. Now, here is what we will do first."

Pasteur paused for a moment, and then outlined in detail what he intended to do. And when Roux and Chamberland understood thoroughly they proceeded to make the first of several tests and experiments that they fervently prayed would lead them to a final solution.

Using a glass tube, Pasteur extracted some of the brain matter of a dog that had died of rabies and then transferred it to a vial and heated it. After that, the matter was mixed with sterilized water and broth. And finally the mixture was injected into twelve rabbits. The results were that almost all of the rabbits contracted hydrophobia and died—first proof that the hydrophobia germ could be found in the brain of a rabies victim!

The next step Pasteur wished to take was to perform the same experiment on the brain of a perfectly well and healthy dog, but for a few days he cringed from the very thought of performing such an experiment. It would necessitate cutting a hole in the dog's skull in order to inject the germ into its brain, and Pasteur simply could not bring himself to cause such pain, even in a dumb animal.

Eventually, though, when his two assistants convinced him that chloroforming the dog into unconsciousness would spare it any pain, Pasteur gave his consent to the experiment. A dog was administered chloroform until unconscious, and then a circle of bone was cut from its skull to expose the brain. The brain was given an injection of the rabies germ mixture, and then the circle of bone was replaced and the skin sewed over it.

The experiment was a success. For two weeks the dog showed no ill effects at all from the deadly injection. Then rabies struck and the dog went mad. Hoarse growls burst from its sagging open mouth, its eyes became bloodshot, its lips drooled greenish foam, and it kept hurling itself blindly at the sides of its cage. In a few hours it crumpled to the floor paralyzed, and death came soon afterward.

The same experiment was tried on four or five more healthy dogs, and when the results proved to be identical Pasteur decided to take his next step. The experimenters had not yet actually seen the hydrophobia germ, but they now knew definitely that it was located in the brain. So Pasteur decided to see if he could control the time it took for the rabies germ to strike.

To accomplish this, he took some matter from the brain of a dead rabid dog and injected it into a rabbit. When that rabbit died he took some of its brain matter and injected it into a second rabbit. Then the same thing to a third and a fourth, and so on, until close to a hundred rabbits had been injected with the brain matter of rabbits that had died from rabies. What he discovered was that each time the germ was more powerful in its effect. The first rabbits injected had died after fourteen days, but the period lessened a little in each case, and the last few rabbits had died only seven days after receiving the hydrophobia injection.

Pasteur now believed that the longer the infectious matter was exposed to the air, the weaker it became. And he now knew for certain that the "germ," which we now know to be a virus, was to be found in the medulla oblongata, the part of the brain that connects with the spinal column. Removing the spinal cord of a rabbit dead from rabies, he suspended it by a thread in a sterile tube filled with air at twenty-three degrees centigrade and plugged at both ends. At the end of fourteen days the dried spinal cord was taken out of the tube and made into a solution which was then injected into several healthy dogs.

The next day the dogs received an injection of solution from a spinal cord dried for thirteen days, the next day another from one that had been dried for twelve days, and so on until the fourteenth day, when the dogs received an injection of the solution of a spinal cord that had been aged for just that one day.

Now it was time for the final and all-important test. All during the fourteen days, the solution-injected dogs had remained quite healthy, and on the vital fourteenth

[116]

day none of them showed any symptoms of rabies. Then each was given a fatal injection of the rabies germ, but the deadly disease did not take effect. Every one of the dogs continued to remain perfectly healthy!

It was a great triumph for Pasteur and his assistants, but that was only the halfway point along the road to their goal. The vaccine Pasteur had discovered would make a dog immune from rabies, but to stamp out the dreaded disease by inoculating every single dog was an impossibility. There were thousands of dogs in Paris and literally millions of them in the rest of France. The cost alone was staggering to the imagination, not to mention the Herculean task of rounding up millions of dogs and keeping them kenneled for fourteen days.

The next step to be taken was to determine if the vaccine not only prevented a dog from getting rabies, but would also prevent it from getting the deadly disease after it had been bitten by a rabid dog.

To make this vital test a rabid dog was put into a cage with two healthy dogs. At the sight of it the two healthy dogs howled in terror, but split seconds later their howls became howls of pain as the rabies-maddened dog hurled itself at them to rip them to shreds. As soon as both healthy dogs had been bitten, Pasteur and his assistants overpowered the rabid one and carried it from their cage to its own.

Then they took out the two bitten dogs. One was given the first of the fourteen vaccine injections, but the other dog's bite wounds were simply cleansed and bound up. At the end of fourteen days the wounded dog that had received an injection each day showed no symptoms of rabies at all, and lived on in perfect health. However, the dog that had simply had its wounds cleaned and bandaged fell ill with rabies and died within a matter of hours.

That test proved what Pasteur had hoped and prayed it would. His rabies vaccine worked both ways. It could be used to protect a dog from rabies before it was bitten by a rabid dog, and it could also be used to prevent rabies after a dog had been bitten.

Dogs, yes, but what about human beings?

That was Louis Pasteur's hope—to save human life from the deadly hydrophobia that still struck terror to the hearts of people all over the world. Only when he had attained that purpose would he fulfill the solemn promise he made to his lost daughters.

But to make his vaccine test on a human being? He didn't dare! Instead of making the subject immune from rabies, the fourteen-day injections might give the patient rabies and kill him. Pasteur had no way of knowing absolutely that it wouldn't, and if by any chance it did, the whole world would curse and condemn him and his murderous "discovery."

For several days, while Roux and Chamberland watched him in helpless silence, Pasteur struggled with his awesome problem, and then made his decision. The human life that must be put in jeopardy for the crucial test would be his own. He would inoculate himself with the deadly disease, and then take the fourteen-day course of injections to see if they would save him.

However, Louis Pasteur did not make the test for final proof on himself. The very next morning a Mrs. Meister, her son Joseph and a grocer named Theodore Vone came to see him in his laboratory. They had come to Paris from Meissengott, in Alsace, and with tears glistening in her eyes and lips trembling the woman told Pasteur the tragic story.

Two days before, on July 4, Joseph Meister had been attacked by a mad dog on his way to school. The small boy had been thrown to the ground by the beast's savage charge. Unable to fight off the animal, he had tried to cover his face with his hands. The mad dog had bitten him repeatedly and might have caused his death on the spot had not a man passing by snatched up a stick and beaten it off.

The dog then ran home to its master, Theodore Vone, but when the grocer tried to chain it up, the dog attacked him and he was finally forced to shoot it. The boy, bitten fourteen times by the dog, was taken to a doctor, who cauterized the wounds but could not give the mother any assurance the treatment would prevent hydrophobia. He strongly advised her to take the boy to Pasteur in Paris. Theodore Vone had come with her because as the owner of the mad dog he felt responsible for the boy's injuries. He had been bitten, too, on the arm, but the dog's fangs had not cut into the skin because of the thickness of his coat sleeve.

When the woman had finished the story, Pasteur examined both the boy and Vone. He assured Vone that he was in no danger; the dog's saliva had obviously been wiped off on the coat sleeve. But the boy's condition was an entirely different story, and cold hands gripped Pasteur's heart as he studied the boy's wounds. Even though they had been cauterized, the wounds were beginning to fester, and the boy's white, strained face and the faint moans that escaped his tight lips were proof that he was in great pain. Pasteur greatly feared that the little fellow would soon fall ill with rabies.

"Our doctor said you had a medicine that would save my boy!" the woman's sudden cry cut through Pasteur's unhappy thoughts. "So I have brought him to you. I beg of you, give it to my boy so that his life will be saved."

Pasteur did not speak for a moment. He wanted with all his heart to save the boy's life; yet in trying, he might succeed only in killing the child. He had not one shred of proof that his vaccine would work on human beings. He only believed it would. Merely believing was not nearly enough to warrant the frightening risk. What if his vaccine failed and the boy died? What if he was one of those few whose bodies were somehow able to hold off the rabies germ? Might the boy not contract the terrible disease from the deliberate injections of the deadly germ? What if a hundred different things?

"Please!" the woman sobbed. "I beg you in God's name, save my boy!"

Pasteur impulsively reached out his hand to touch hers in a comforting gesture. Struggling to keep the anxiety out of his own voice, he told her that his vaccine had proved its worth only on dogs so far—that it had yet to be tested on a human being, and that although he believed it would work, it might not and the boy would die. He also told her that he simply could not make a decision right then, but that he would dress the boy's wounds, that he would get them a place to stay, and that she was to bring the boy back to see him at five o'clock that afternoon. He would have by then made his decision what to do.

When the visitors had left, Pasteur got in touch with two men he hoped might help him in making his decision. One was Dr. Vulpian, a member of the rabies commission set up to investigate Pasteur's vaccine, and the other was Dr. Grancher, one of France's leading bacteriologists. They came as quickly as they could to the laboratory, where Pasteur told them the whole story in detail. He spoke of the boy's wounds, already starting to fester, and of the mother's plea that he use his vaccine on her son for the first time. Finally, he asked them if they thought the situation warranted his administering the dog vaccine to a human being.

Neither of the doctors advanced any opinion at once. Instead, they waited until Mrs. Meister returned with her son at five o'clock and they were able to examine the boy for themselves. When they had completed their examination they went into another room with Pasteur and told him what they thought. Their judgment was that the boy should be given the vaccine.

They were convinced that the boy had been given the dreaded disease by the dog's bites, and that he would almost certainly fall ill with hydrophobia. The cauterizing of the wounds, which had not been done until twelve hours after they were inflicted, had not helped at all. If Pasteur gave the boy the vaccine it might possibly fail, but without the vaccine the boy would almost inevitably die. He was doomed, they believed, unless the vaccine could save him.

Although both learned doctors advised him to give Joseph the vaccine, Louis Pasteur still hesitated. If he tried and failed, the boy's death would be on his conscience for as long as he lived. But another thought came to him. If he did nothing and the boy died, would not the fact that he had not tried to save the lad be on his conscience for the rest of his life? That thought forced his decision.

"Thank you," he said to the two famous doctors. "I will go and prepare the vaccine."

On that evening of July 6, 1885, Louis Pasteur gave little Joseph Meister his first injection of the rabies vaccine. It was done in a room of the old Rollin College, where Pasteur had arranged for the boy and his mother to stay. The injection was a spinal cord solution of the fourteen-day type, but the boy progressed so rapidly that on July sixteenth Pasteur gave him his final injection—of a solution of spinal cord aged only one day.

All those days and nights Pasteur lived in terror that his vaccine might fail. He knew that hydrophobia could strike swiftly and at any time. Each time he went to see Joseph Meister, it was in dread of finding the boy in the grip of the terrible disease, gasping for air and writhing in pain. But his prayers were answered. Thirty-one days after his first inoculation, little Joseph went home with his mother, completely cured.

The news of Louis Pasteur's great triumph thrilled all France. A national holiday was declared in his honor, and after he had returned from a short rest in the country, parents with children bitten by rabid animals started coming to him from all over the world. He and his assistants worked night and day preparing the precious vaccine and administering it to their patients, some of whom had come from such far-off countries as Russia and the United States. In the matter of just a few weeks Pasteur gave his vaccine inoculations to a total of three hundred and fifty people bitten by rabid dogs. All but one continued to go on living in fine health.

The one was little, nine-year-old Louise Pelletier, who was not brought to him until thirty-seven days after she had been bitten by a dog. One look at the poor little thing and Pasteur knew in his heart that her case was hopeless. Her terrible wounds were in such a condition that he knew hydrophobia might show itself at any moment. Nevertheless, he did everything in his power to save the little girl. As a matter of fact, at first she showed such marked improvement from the inoculations that she was able to go home, but the dreaded disease still had too strong a grip on her and she fell ill again.

Pasteur rushed from Paris to her home in the country and did everything he possibly could to ward off the end, but a second series of inoculations did not take effect, and the miracle he prayed for in his heart did not come to pass. Long, long ago he had sat by the bedsides of each of his typhoid-stricken daughters and watched them die. Now he sat by little Louise Pelletier's bedside and watched death win the battle again. It was his only failure in his battle against hydrophobia.

High honors from all of the world were again showered upon Louis Pasteur for his great work. A large sum of money was contributed by the people of France, and by people of a dozen other nationalities, to build and name in his honor the Pasteur Institute in Paris. Several small towns and countless streets in countries throughout the world were renamed for him. The highborn and the lowborn across the face of the earth acclaimed him aloud or in their hearts for the truly great man he was.

At long last Louis Pasteur had fulfilled the promise he made at the burial of each of his three young daughters, for he had fought and beaten one of mankind's greatest scourges. To this day, Pasteur's remains the only treatment for that dread disease.

7

The Yellow Killer

WALTER REED
(1851–1902)

One day in the late Spring of 1648 a dirty-gray fog rolled in off the waters of the Gulf to envelop an area of land now known as the State of Yucatan, in Mexico. In those days Yucatan was populated by Mayan Indians, although subject to Spain, and when the elder members of the tribes saw the people fall ill with a mysterious disease, a great fear clutched at their hearts. "It is the sign of death!" they cried out. "It has been decreed that we must die!"

The younger people may have secretly scoffed at the fears of their elders, but they did not do so for long. A month later, in June, the mysterious disease swept north into the city of Campeche. Without any warning people suffered severe hemorrhages and violent attacks of vomiting, their skin turned a jaundice yellow and a few days later they died like flies. In a matter of two or three weeks the entire city was in a state of utter chaos.

What the mysterious disease was, where it had come from, and how it struck, no one knew or could even guess. Nothing like it had ever struck Yucatan before. There seemed to be nothing anybody could do to stem it. And nothing at all could be done for those who fell victims to it. They were doomed. In an attempt to stop it at least from spreading beyond the city limits, guards were posted on all roads to prevent anyone from leaving Campeche, but that did no good.

During the month of August the Yellow Fever, the name it was given because of the color it turned the skin of its victims, struck the city of Merida, a hundred miles away. Because of the hue of the sick people's regurgitation, the Spanish called it "vomito negro," the black vomit. And in a little over a week's time there was hardly a man, woman or child who had not fallen ill from it. Literally thousands died in both Campeche and Merida, and then just as swiftly as it had appeared the yellow killer disappeared from the face of the land.

But only to soon strike elsewhere!

In 1649, just one year later, it struck the island of Cuba, and before it had run its terrible course over a third of the Cuban population had died from it.

From Cuba it swept across the Caribbean Sea and for

some unknown reason struck the tiny Windward Island of St. Lucia. A British fleet was stationed there at the time, and of its complement of some fourteen hundred men less than one hundred survived the epidemic. Many of the natives on the island also fell ill and died, for the Yellow Killer was no respecter of race, creed or color.

Nor was it any respecter of geographical location. After a lapse of some fifty years the mysterious disease suddenly struck the southern and eastern borders of the United States. It struck not only once but more than a hundred times in the next two hundred years. Great cities like Philadelphia and New Orleans were hit particularly hard. In Philadelphia one out of every nine people infected died. And in New Orleans, the number of dead from Yellow Fever was estimated to be over eight thousand people in the space of a few weeks.

However, cities were not the only targets for the Yellow Killer. In the year of 1878 it went tearing up through the Mississippi Valley, leaving in its wake a total of over fourteen thousand dead people.

What was it? What caused it? Where did it come from? How did it strike? What could be done to prevent it? And, most important, what could be done to save those stricken by it? For two hundred years there were no correct answers to those questions. True, there were plenty of answers advanced. All kinds of them.

As Yellow Fever seemed to strike more often along the waterfront than inland some thought it must be caused by river mud. Or perhaps it was caused by the decaying carcasses of animals. Or perhaps it was a deadly fungus, not visible to the naked eye, blown in off the Gulf of Mexico. Or perhaps filth subject to intense heat and high humidity became mingled with the air and became a sort of Yellow Fever Wind, a miasma, that doomed all those it blew against. Or perhaps it came from fruit such as lemons, bananas and oranges kept stored too long.

Hundreds of answers were offered by men of medicine as well as by the man in the street, but not one of them could be proved correct. In the meantime the Yellow Killer went its deadly way, striking again and again, bringing terror to the hearts of thousands of people. Whenever it struck, life-long friends in the inflicted area would not dare shake hands with each other when they met on the street, lest one might have Yellow Fever and so give it to the other. People would shutter their windows, lock their doors and refuse to allow any outsider to enter. Parents took their children out of school, and working men would refuse to show up on the job until the yellow killer had taken its toll of dead and moved on.

So it went until 1900, when a forty-nine year old major in the United States Army Medical Corps was assigned the task of solving the mystery of Yellow Fever and, if possible, finding ways to stamp it out.

The major's name was Walter Reed. He was born in the hills of Virginia, September 13, 1851, and at a very early age he had dedicated his life to medicine. As a matter of fact, at the age of only seventeen he passed the required examinations while attending the University of

Virginia and was awarded his M.D. degree. He continued
his studies at New York's Bellevue Hospital Medical College, and later served on the staffs of other New York
hospitals.

However, when he eventually set up his own practice,
he made the sad discovery that it was not his lack of
medical knowledge that kept people from his door, but
rather his extreme youth. His would-be patients were
used to elderly doctors, and were highly reluctant to put
their faith and trust in a twenty-one year old youth.
Nevertheless, he stuck at it for another year before he
finally faced up to the fact that his youth was just too
much against him, and closed his office.

However, for some time young Reed had been seriously considering the idea of entering the Army Medical
Corps, so when he closed his office he set his sights on
that goal. Before he could take the examinations,
though, it was necessary for him to bone up on several
subjects he had studied only briefly while in college.
This he did, and, after missing two examination dates
because of sickness, he finally sat for his examinations
in June of 1875. He passed and was awarded a commission as a first lieutenant in the U.S. Army Medical
Corps, with the classification of assistant surgeon.

Then began some twenty-five years of service, many
of them spent at lonely Army posts in western Indian
territory. He performed his duties well, rose in rank, and
in time was transferred back east for special study at
Johns Hopkins Hospital, in Baltimore. In 1893, he was
ordered to Washington, D.C., where he was given the

rank of major and the classification of a full surgeon and appointed a director of the Army Medical Library. In addition, he was made a professor of bacteriology at the United States Medical School. Then came 1900 and the greatest challenge of his entire medical career.

Although over the years Yellow Fever had struck at many different places in the Western Hemisphere, the Island of Cuba had been hit by it the greatest number of times. For that reason Cuba was believed to be the "home" of the deadly disease. However, that island's nearness to the United States was not the only reason why the Army Medical Corps decided to take steps to determine the true nature of the deadly disease and combat it.

The Spanish-American War had just ended, and during the last year of the war an alarming number of American soldiers had met death not from bullets but from Yellow Fever, or "Yellow Jack," as they called it. One artillery battalion alone had lost a third of its men to Yellow Fever. And though the war was over there was still a large force of American troops occupying Cuba, with a Yellow Fever epidemic there at the moment on the rise, rather than abating.

So on June 25, 1900, the U.S. Army Surgeon-General appointed a Yellow Fever Board, placed Major Walter Reed in charge of it, and ordered him to Cuba to see what he could do about the situation. The other members of the Board were Aristides Agramonte, a Cuban; James Carroll, who had worked with Major Reed; and Jesse Lazear, who was already on medical duty at the

Columbia Barracks Hospital at Los Quemados, some miles along the coast from Havana.

Shortly after Major Reed arrived in Cuba he went to visit a Dr. Carlos J. Finlay, who lived in Havana. Dr. Finlay was quite an old man, and for the last twenty-five years he had been devoting a major part of his time in an attempt to prove that his own theory on Yellow Fever was correct. He believed that it was not filth, ghostly winds, fog, or any other environmental condition that brought the Yellow Killer, but a mosquito. What's more, he believed it to be a domestic mosquito that lived where people lived. In short, it was the female of a species called *Aëdes aegypti*. Unfortunately, though, after twenty-five years of breeding his own mosquitoes, studying their life cycles, and making hundreds of experiments and tests, he had been unable to produce absolute proof, and so nobody put any stock in his claim.

However, it was well known to Major Reed, as it was to most of the medical world, that mosquitoes did spread malaria from one person to another. As a matter of fact, at the time of Major Reed's arrival in Cuba, several American soldiers who had actually died from Yellow Fever were being listed in Army records as having died from what was called pernicious malaria. Dr. Finlay, after being permitted to examine some of them, had insisted it was not malaria, but they still wouldn't believe him! That is, not until Aristides Agramonte also made an examination and agreed with Dr. Finlay.

Major Reed was very much impressed by his talk with Dr. Finlay, and he was inclined to believe that the

Aëdes aegypti mosquito might be the enemy he was seeking out. But there was one thing that stopped him from accepting Dr. Finlay's theory completely. The volunteers Dr. Finlay had used in his experiments might very easily have contracted Yellow Fever before they were bitten by the doctor's testing mosquitoes.

However, all Dr. Finlay told him was of great interest to Major Reed. And shortly after that visit, there was a Yellow Fever case at an Army post at Santa Clara which gave him even more food for thought. On June 6 an American soldier had been placed in a guardhouse there to serve out a ninety-day punishment sentence. On July 12 he fell ill with Yellow Fever, and six days later he was dead. He had not been let out of the guardhouse even once, so he could not possibly have contracted the deadly disease on the outside. But eight other soldiers also serving time in the guardhouse did not catch Yellow Fever. Not even the one of them who was now sleeping in the bunk used by the dead soldier!

That single case pointed up several facts for Major Reed. For one thing, Yellow Fever evidently was not transmitted from one victim to another by contact. And it was not transmitted in food, either. In that guardhouse all nine prisoners had come in contact with one another countless times. They had all eaten the same cooked food, and they had all had contact with the guards on duty watching them. All had breathed the same air, but only one had contracted Yellow Fever and died.

For Major Reed there seemed to be just one answer to that riddle. The dead soldier's bunk had been near an unscreened window, and a disease-bearing mosquito must have flown in and bitten him and not any of the eight others.

It became Major Reed's firm conviction that a thorough investigation of Dr. Finlay's *Aëdes aegypti* mosquito theory should be made. It was begun immediately, and under the supervision of Jesse Lazear, because Major Reed was suddenly called back to Washington for consultation on another Medical Corps problem.

Jesse Lazear began his work by obtaining mosquito eggs and hatching them by various methods. It was his intention to let them become full grown and then conduct the first series of tests. He placed a full grown mosquito in a test tube, held the open end against the skin of a Yellow Fever victim, let the mosquito take as much of the victim's blood as it wanted. He did this with several mosquitoes and then let those same mosquitoes bite eight members of his hospital group, including himself, who had volunteered to serve as guinea pigs for the experiment.

All eight were bitten by the fever-infected mosquitoes, but nothing happened. Not a single man came down with the malady, or even with anything resembling it. The zero results of the experiment greatly puzzled Jesse Lazear until the thought occurred to him that the element of time might be an important factor. In other words, it was quite possible that a certain number of days had to pass before a mosquito which had bitten a Yellow Fever victim could pass it along when it bit a perfectly healthy person.

After some study and calculation, Lazear judged the time period to be between ten and fourteen days. He then conducted a second test, but in secret. He let a mosquito that had bitten a Yellow Fever patient in the hospital twelve days before bite himself, but didn't tell anybody about it.

The heroic act proved Dr. Finlay's theory to be true, but it cost Jesse Lazear his life. He fell violently ill with Yellow Fever and died in a week's time. Not until after his death, when his notes on his investigation of Dr. Finlay's theory were read, was it discovered that Jesse Lazear had deliberately used himself as a guinea pig. When he had fallen ill it was thought that he had been accidentally bitten by one of the Yellow Fever mosquitoes in his laboratory.

There had been two other volunteers for that same test. For them the result did not turn out to be death. One of them was James Carroll, a member of the Yellow Fever Board. For two or three days after he was bitten by the Yellow Fever-laden mosquito, he showed no ill effects at all. On the fourth day, though, he was too weak to get out of bed and the next day he came down with Yellow Fever. For almost two weeks he hovered on the brink of death, and then his condition slowly started to improve. At the end of some six weeks he was able to get out of bed and fully recovered.

The other volunteer was a young soldier by the name

of Dean, who for some strange reason contracted only a mild case of the disease. As a matter of fact, he was completely recovered and back on duty long before James Carroll was even sitting up in bed.

In October of that year of 1900 Major Reed returned to Cuba and once more took active charge of the Yellow Fever investigation. He carefully studied all the detailed reports of the Board's work thus far, and particularly the reports on Jesse Lazear, James Carroll and Private Dean. Jesse Lazear's death had of course saddened him greatly for they had been close friends; but of all the information gathered, what interested him the most was the case of Private Dean.

In Reed's opinion, Dean was the only one who had contracted Yellow Fever under definitely controlled conditions, not by chance. And that would prove Dr. Finlay's theory to be true. James Carroll had left the camp a couple of times, and also moved about the camp freely, in the three days before he was taken sick. And because poor Jesse Lazear had conducted the test on himself in secret it was impossible to tell whether that particular intentional bite or an accidental bite by some other mosquito had infected him with Yellow Fever and brought about his death.

In the case of Private Dean, however, there was no reason to doubt and wonder. It had been clearcut proof of Dr. Finlay's theory. At the time Dean was bitten, he was in the hospital undergoing treatment for another ailment. The day he was bitten by one of Jesse Lazear's mosquitoes he had been discharged from the hospital and returned to his post in the camp. Then two days later, not having once gone outside the camp, he had returned to the hospital ill with Yellow Fever.

When Major Reed had read all the detailed reports and studied all the facts, he became sure beyond all possible doubt in his mind that the mosquito *Aëdes aegypti* was the carrier of the deadly Yellow Fever germ. He then presented himself before General Leonard Wood, commander of all the American forces in Cuba, and requested permission to set up an experimental camp where complete control over all further tests could be maintained. He told the general he wanted to set up the camp in a sunny open area well away from the Columbia Camp, and away from any town. He also wanted to have two separate wooden buildings constructed, so well screened that no mosquitoes inside could get out, and none outside could get in. In addition, he wanted to pay five hundred dollars to every man, Cuban or American, who volunteered for his tests.

General Wood agreed to all of Major Reed's requests, and work was begun immediately on building the experimental camp on the site Reed had selected. The camp was named Camp Lazear.

High priority was given to the building program, and by the middle of November the job was completed. Tents and all the accompanying facilities had been set up for the group of sixteen men who would run the camp. The two special wooden buildings had been constructed exactly as Major Reed had requested them to be.

They were simply called Building No. 1 and Building No. 2. The two were built a hundred yards apart. No. 1 was purposely badly ventilated, but tightly screened so that not a single mosquito could get into it. In it were placed all kinds of articles, clothing and blankets which had been used by Yellow Fever victims. If volunteers living in No. 1 Building did not catch Yellow Fever, then Major Reed would have his proof that Yellow Fever was not transmitted by personal contact in any form.

Building No. 2, referred to as the infected mosquito building, was the one on which Major Reed placed his greatest hopes for success in solving the problem. It was divided into two sections by a tight-fitting screen, and both sections were well ventilated. In one section there would be volunteers to be bitten by Yellow Fever infected mosquitoes, and in the other section, tightly screened so that no mosquito could possibly enter, would be volunteers who would not be intentionally bitten by infected mosquitoes. If the latter did not catch Yellow Fever, then Major Reed would have additional proof of Doctor Finlay's theory.

By the middle of November, Camp Lazear was all set to go into action, but people who might volunteer to be guinea pigs were not. The five-hundred-dollar bonus was tempting, but as one soldier expressed it, "What good does five hundred dollars do you in Heaven?" And as for the Cuban people there was an angry uproar when the offer was published in the Havana newspapers. The American military was publicly charged with offering five hundred dollars so that they could play at murder.

In time, though, volunteers did come forward. The first two were young American soldiers stationed at Columbia Camp. They were Private John J. Moran, and Private John R. Kissinger—and both volunteered in the interests of science, refusing to accept the reward. They started the ball rolling. As soon as the word of what they had done got out, other soldiers offered themselves, and so did a number of Cuban civilians. As a result, by the end of November Major Reed and his group had all the volunteers they needed for both Building No. 1, and Building No. 2.

After a thorough examination to make sure both were in good physical shape, Moran and Kissinger were quarantined for a couple of weeks to make sure they had not already contracted Yellow Fever. Then they were placed in the section of Building No. 2 containing the infected mosquitoes and were bitten several times. But nothing happened. For three weeks both soldiers remained in perfect health, and Major Reed and his associates were at a complete loss to understand why. Rechecking every detail of the painstaking experiment, they finally came up with what they thought had to be the answer—the weather. It had been a bit on the chilly side, and apparently under those conditions the bite of a disease-infected mosquito had no damaging effects.

At the end of those baffling three weeks, though, the weather became considerably warmer. Moran, Kissinger, and three Cubans who had since volunteered were again bitten by infected mosquitoes. This time Yellow Fever did strike.

Private Kissinger was the first to fall ill with the killer disease. Three days after he had been bitten he complained of severe chills, terrible headache and a backache; his temperature soared up close to one hundred and three degrees. In Major Reed's mind there was no question: Kissinger had been hit by Yellow Fever. However, the major had no wish for the skeptics—and they included just about the entire medical world—to simply accept his say-so as fact. So he invited a large group of Havana doctors out to Camp Lazear to see for themselves.

The Havana doctors did come and saw for themselves, and although at first they refused to express an opinion, they were eventually forced to admit that Kissinger was sick with Yellow Fever given to him by an infected mosquito. But Major Reed did not stop there. He conducted the visiting doctors over to Building No. 1 where three other volunteers, a Dr. Cook and Privates Folk and Jernegan, had been living for three weeks, using pillows, blankets, clothing, and food utensils that had been used by Yellow Fever victims. The visiting doctors examined all three men and found them to be in perfect health. What those doctors had been saying was just "a crazy old man's theory" wasn't anything of the sort now. It was now proven fact, and they reluctantly admitted it.

Reluctantly, perhaps, because, after all, only one of the five volunteers bitten by Yellow Fever laden mosquitoes had fallen ill with the disease. The three Cubans and Private Moran were still in good health when the group of Havana doctors made their inspection. But shortly after the doctors returned to Havana, Major Reed obtained further proof of Dr. Finlay's theory. The three Cuban volunteers came down with Yellow Fever and along with Private Kissinger were taken to the Columbia Barracks Hospital where they would receive the best of care. For a while the lives of all four hung in the balance, but eventually they all recovered their health.

Of the original five to take the bite test, only Private Moran failed to contract Yellow Fever—that is, right at the start. He was given the test a second time and still continued to remain in good health, but when he was given the bite test for the third time he finally fell ill with the dreaded disease. He was also rushed to the Columbia Barracks Hospital, and like the other four he, too, hovered between life and death for ten days or more before he started back on the road to complete recovery.

All in all a total of nine Americans and five Cubans took Major Reed's test, contracted Yellow Fever, and were brought back to complete recovery by the splendid doctors at Columbia Barracks Hospital. Not a single volunteer for the bite test lost his life. Neither did a single volunteer who lived in the screened-off, mosquito-free room right next to the infected mosquito room. And neither did a single volunteer who lived all during the crucial test period in the filthy, poorly ventilated, infected clothing room in Building No. 1.

The critical tests were a great triumph for Major Reed

and to a considerable degree for old Dr. Carlos J. Finlay, who had tried unsuccessfully for twenty-five long years to get medical men to accept his theory. And it should be noted that Major Reed was not the type of man who would ask others to do what he was afraid to do himself. Several times during the Yellow Fever Board's investigation he had offered himself as a guinea pig, but because of his tremendous value to the entire operation he was not permitted to run the risk.

So at long last the mystery of Yellow Fever had been solved. The enemy was the deadly female *Aëdes aegypti* mosquito. But finding who the enemy was was only half the battle. The other half was finding ways and means of stamping out Yellow Fever once and for all—a battle, incidentally, that is still being waged in some remote parts of the world.

On Major Reed's recommendation, a Major Kean was assigned the task of drawing up plans for an all-out effort to stamp out the Yellow Fever mosquito in Havana, a city of over three hundred thousand people. And Major William C. Gorgas, who had served in the Spanish-American War as Sanitation Officer, was placed in charge of carrying out the mosquito attack.

Believing that the breeding places of the deadly mosquito were places of filth and pools of stagnant water, Major Gorgas organized a vast Havana clean-up squad of some two thousand men. Divided up into small groups, they went to work with a will, dragging away dead animals found in streets and alleys, clearing the streets of all garbage and refuse, burning rubbish, and repairing leaking plumbing all over the city. Being a very energetic person, Major Gorgas often kept his squads hard at work for as many as sixteen hours a day.

Unfortunately, though, all that back-breaking work didn't check the amount of Yellow Fever in Havana in the slightest. As a matter of fact, the deadly disease actually gained in the number of its victims. And the oddest thing of it all was that more Yellow Fever broke out in places that Major Gorgas' men cleaned up than in places they had yet to clean.

Not until some time later was the reason for that strange circumstance discovered. It was not because Major Gorgas' squads hadn't done a good clean-up job, but because large numbers of country people moving into the city naturally chose to settle in the cleanest places. A great number of Havana residents had become somewhat immune to Yellow Fever, having lived with it for so long, but not so the people who moved in from the country. They were ripe for the deadly disease and the Yellow Fever mosquitoes fell upon them in droves!

As a result of the clean-up campaign, Major Gorgas adopted another method of attack. And, incidentally, it was old Dr. Finlay who through Major Reed got Major Gorgas to try a different kind of attack. As Dr. Finlay pointed out, garbage, filth and pools of water were not the causes of the disease. The villain was the mosquito. So forget the garbage in the streets, he counseled, and concentrate on killing the mosquito and preventing any of its larvae from being hatched.

The new type of attack for Major Gorgas and his two

thousand men got good results right from the start. Every place that might contain mosquito larvae was sprayed with petroleum, which instantly killed the unhatched killers, for larval mosquitoes cannot breathe under a film of oil. All open containers of water, such as fire buckets and cisterns, were covered with a thin coating of kerosene, as were wells, since the water was drawn from the bottom of the well. There were many other death-to-the-mosquito measures taken by Major Gorgas and his men, and in time they began to pay off handsomely.

In March of 1901, when Major Gorgas began his campaign to stamp out the Yellow Fever mosquito in Havana, there were over a hundred deaths from the disease in the city. As a matter of fact, for more than a hundred and fifty years the city had not seen a day go by when there hadn't been at least one death from Yellow Fever. But Major Gorgas and his men soon changed that unfavorable record. Beginning with April first, the city of Havana did not see a single death from Yellow Fever for a period of ninety-one days. During the month of July there was one death from the disease reported, and the Yellow Fever death toll for the months of August and September was four. But after September there was not one death for a period of nine months!

That marked the beginning of the end of Yellow Fever in Cuba, and the beginning of the end of it in many other parts of the world. Major Reed and his brave associates had put the finger on the identity of the Yellow Killer, and Major Gorgas had devised and perfected the techniques for stamping it out of existence. Incidentally, Cuba was, in a sense, only the beginning for Major Gorgas. He was later to be sent to Panama, where uncounted thousands working on the building of the Panama Canal had died from Yellow Fever. It was a far tougher job than the one he had tackled in Cuba for many reasons, one of them being political bickering. However, he stuck to his job, and in time he completely rid the Canal Zone of the Yellow Fever mosquito, and the Big Ditch was dug to completion without any further loss of life from Yellow Fever. No longer was it a menace to be capitalized in men's minds.

Having successfully completed the job he had come to do in Cuba, Major Reed returned to Washington, D.C., in February, 1901. He resumed his old duties as professor of bacteriology at the Army Medical School, but not before he was awarded high honors for his splendid achievement in Cuba. He was given honorary degrees from several universities, and medical men all over the world respected him for his great work.

But death was near for Major Walter Reed. Less than two years after he had returned home from Cuba, Major Reed was stricken with appendicitis. He was operated on, but peritonitis developed and the doctors were helpless to save his life. He died on November 23, 1902. In 1909 a lasting tribute to the memory of Major Walter Reed was dedicated. It was the now internationally known Walter Reed Hospital, located in Washington, D.C.

8

The Invisible Marauders

JOSEPH LISTER
(1827–1912)

In 1865 Louis Pasteur wrote a paper for the journal of the French Académie des Sciences in which he described in detail his discovery of what caused damaging fermentation in wines. That discovery saved the French wine-producing industry from complete ruin, and in the paper Pasteur wrote about it was a key which a man in far-off Glasgow used to unlock the door to one of the greatest triumphs in all medical history.

The name of that man in Scotland was Joseph Lister, and at the time he was the professor of surgery at the Royal Infirmary, University of Glasgow. Born of Quaker parents at Upton, Essex County, England, on April 5,

1827, Lister knew even at the early age of ten that his one desire in life was to become a surgeon.

After attending Quaker schools at Hitchin and Tottenham, young Lister went to London to enter University College of London and began his medical studies under the noted physiologist William Sharpey. Professor Sharpey was a close friend of Lister's father, a well-to-do manufacturer of microscope lenses, and he kept a watchful eye on the young medical student. It did not take him very long to realize that Joseph Lister was not only a keen student but possessed a probing, questioning mind that refused to accept things as fact simply because those more learned than he accepted them.

In those days, surgery in hospitals could almost be called human butchery. It was an ordeal of unspeakable terror and agony for any patient to go under the surgeon's knife. Not, let it be hastily said, because surgeons were a group of cruel, sadistic men. It was because they simply did not know enough about surgery techniques to be able to spare their patients any pain. Such a thing as anesthesia was totally unknown until 1846, and the reasons for gangrene, erysipelas and pyemia were also unknown. Whenever any of these complications developed after an operation, they were simply regarded as "hospital diseases," something no one could do anything about.

Medical men knew nothing in those days about antiseptics. Speed was what counted most with the surgeons. The faster they operated the less agony for the patient. Also, the more people they operated on in

[146]

the course of a day, the more money in fees they made. Cleanliness in any degree simply wasn't considered. A surgeon's coat with its collection of stains from the operating table was a mark of his profession, and he wore it all the time in the hospital and outside, too. As a result, a time-worn cliché was proved true thousands and thousands of times over! "The operation was a success, but the patient died."

During the time Joseph Lister was a medical student at University College, and after he had graduated to University College Hospital, post-operative setbacks and death seemed a challenge to him. Whenever he got the chance, he asked one of his superiors why gangrene, erysipelas, and such things developed after an operation, and he always got the same answer. The accepted theory was that those things were caused by an "unknown poison" in the air.

That answer Joseph Lister could not accept. In his mind he was sure there must be other reasons—tangible ones you could put your finger on—but what they were he had not the faintest idea. He made a promise to himself, however, to try and find out those reasons if it was humanly possible to do so.

Shortly before he was awarded his medical degree in surgery in 1853, Lister was to witness an operation which made a profound impression on him. It was one of the first operations performed in England with the use of ether as an anesthetic. For the first time in his life he saw a patient spared the pain of the surgeon's knife. To him it was a wonderful advance in surgery, and not only because it spared the patient pain. It also permitted the operating surgeon to take more time with the operation and, by so doing, perhaps prevent some of the very common, harmful developments afterward. But when he spoke of that to his colleagues and his superiors they looked at him as if he were a crazy man.

"Take our time!" they snorted. "Have you suddenly gone insane? Speed is what will gain you a reputation as a good surgeon. And money! If you waste a lot of time on an operation that can be performed in a few minutes, you'll soon have jolly few patients, and that's a fact!"

Nevertheless, Joseph Lister clung to the belief that if a surgeon took his time performing an operation it might help. And he also clung to the belief that there must be definite reasons for the terrible death rate in and after the operating room. He still had those beliefs when in September of 1853 he went to the University of Edinburgh, Scotland, to continue his studies under James Syme, professor of the School of Surgery there, and one of the most learned surgeons in the British Isles.

One thing about the School of Surgery that appealed to young Lister was that the wards and the operating room were kept much cleaner, and far better ventilated, than those at the University College Hospital. It should be said, though, that none of it was due in any part to Professor Syme's desire to guard and protect the health of the patients; it was simply that he personally hated dirt and foul smells. But Lister was impressed, and he made a resolution that if he ever became the head of a hospital he would certainly put cleanliness and good ventilation high on his list of musts.

During the next two years Lister learned a great deal under Professor Syme, and he rapidly proved himself to be quite an accomplished surgeon despite his years. In 1855 when he was only twenty-eight he was made a Lecturer at the University of Edinburgh, and was also made a Fellow of the Royal College of Surgeons in Edinburgh. In 1856 he married Agnes Syme, his professor's daughter, who would prove to be of great inspiration to him in the history-making achievements yet to come.

In 1860, he finally got the chance to test some of his own ideas that he had been unable to do anything about while working under Professor Syme at Edinburgh. He was appointed Professor of Systematic Surgery at the University of Glasgow. At first, he simply taught classes and conducted a small practice in surgery in his spare time. But at the end of the year he was made head of the Royal Infirmary and was able to, figuratively speaking, roll up his sleeves and go to work.

The surgical unit of the infirmary was a nice enough looking building from the outside, but when he went inside, Dr. Lister was appalled by what he saw (and smelled). The poorly lighted rooms were filthy almost beyond belief, and the whole place was crowded with far too many patients, waiting to be examined, waiting to be operated on, or just waiting to die.

After making an inspection tour of the entire infirmary, Lister ordered that the ward floors be cleaned of their filth, the windows washed and clean sheets put on the beds. In several cases he ordered brand-new mattresses for the beds. His housecleaning orders brought howls of protest that none of it was necessary, and, more important, that the hospital couldn't afford the expense. However, Lister insisted, and little by little he got what he demanded.

While at Edinburgh Dr. Lister had done a considerable amount of research on pyemia (blood poisoning), erysipelas (skin inflammation), and gangrene (skin and flesh decay) in an effort to determine the causes of those so-called "hospital diseases." Using a microscope with one of his father's finest lenses, he had spent hours studying smears of human blood, inflamed skin, and bits of infected flesh, but succeeded in learning very little— and nothing that gave him any idea as to the causes of the three hospital diseases.

He continued his research work at Glasgow University, but with not much better success. True, he learned some things, but each time he tried to extend his knowledge of some minor point he had discovered, he was unable to make any headway at all. In the meantime, though, he continued to do everything he could to make his hospital wards halfway decent places for sick and injured people. Unfortunately, his clean-floors-and-sheets crusade did not diminish the infirmary death rate to any noticeable degree. The hospital diseases continued to take their toll, and far too many patients who survived a successful operation died a little later.

There was one type of injury in particular that mystified him because of the high rate of deaths resulting from it. That was the compound fracture. In a simple bone fracture, the bones were cracked or slightly split, and they could usually be made to knit together in time, with the bone as strong as it was before. A compound fracture, however, was a definite break, with the jagged ends of the bones often sticking up through the skin. They, too, could be set and made to knit in time, but not so the flesh wounds the broken points of bone had caused.

In many cases, the wound would become badly inflamed and pus would form in it. In time, gangrene would set in, and eventually the patient would die. Why? Why did forty-five out of every one hundred compound fracture patients eventually die? Why did the wounds sometimes heal and scab perfectly, and yet there would be inflammation and pus formed around the tiny holes made by the silk used in sewing up the wound? Joseph Lister did not know; he could only guess. Something must have got into the wound, or had been there all the time, that caused the pyemia, erysipelas, or gangrene. It was not the often-blamed mysterious poisoning in the air; of that he was almost certain. It had to be something else, but *what* he simply did not know.

And then, in the early part of 1865, he was given the aforementioned key to the mysterious unknown. An infirmary colleague came to him one day with a copy of that month's journal published by the French Académie des Sciences. "There is an article in this by a French chemist named Louis Pasteur," the colleague said. "I think you might be interested in reading it."

Dr. Lister thanked the man, put the journal to one side on his desk, and continued with his day's work at the infirmary. That night he took the journal home with him and read the article after supper. The evening was one he would never forget.

From Louis Pasteur's article he learned that it was germs, or microbes—all about in the air and on everything—that got into wine and milk and caused them to turn bad. Two hundred years before, a Dutchman, one Anton van Leeuwenhoek, had first seen microbes with his homemade microscope, and had called them *animalculae*. But Pasteur called them germs, and in his article he told of how they bred and what they bred on. He said that they were actual living things that could get into unprotected things and cause all kinds of chemical changes.

Lister read the article several times, almost memorizing every word, and when he finally put the journal down, he was more excited than he had been at any other time in his life. One reason was because it was only then that he realized he too had seen these destroying microbes under his own microscope. Two or three times when he had studied bits of inflamed skin or gangrenous flesh under his microscope he had noticed several tiny objects no bigger than a pin hole, but he hadn't known what they were. Now he knew! They had been some of Pasteur's germs that floated down out of the air to do some otherwise unexplained damage!

To make doubly sure that he now really was on the

right track, Lister performed some of the experiments Pasteur described in detail in his article, and obtained the same results. When those experiments were completed, he turned his attention from microbes in milk, sugared water and so forth, to microbes in smears of wound pus, infected skin, and gangrenous flesh. As before, he saw the strange, minute things under his microscope, but this time he knew what he was looking at. The one thing he didn't know yet was what to do about them.

In his work with wine and milk Pasteur had found that heat and filtration prevented the destroying bacteria from doing their work. But heat and filtration could not be used in the case of human wounds. There had to be something else to kill the germs, and the name for it was *antiseptic.*

An antiseptic was needed, but what? What would kill deadly germs in a wound, but wouldn't also destroy the flesh or infect the blood? Dr. Lister spent some time wondering about that. Then one day, quite by chance, he came across an article in a paper telling how the sanitation department of a nearby city had been able to rid its air of the stench of a garbage dump by spraying the dump with carbolic acid. That caused him to wonder if the carbolic acid spray had eliminated the stench because it had destroyed what *caused* the stench—in short, the rotting decay in the dump caused by billions and billions of germs. If so, would carbolic acid destroy deadly germs in a human wound without harming the wound?

There was only one way to find that out, by a test on

a human being—possibly one of the patients in the infirmary suffering from a compound fracture? Not just any patient, however. Dr. Lister was anything but a heartless man. Though he did not really believe there would be any danger, he selected a patient for his test whose wounds were already inflamed and becoming gangrenous, and who was almost certainly doomed to die.

The all-important first test took place in March, 1865, and it was a failure—not, however, through any fault of Lister's. He had carefully washed the wound with carbolic acid, and then applied cloths soaked in the acid; but what he did not know at the time, and could not know, was that the man was already too far gone from loss of blood, and from the effects of the infection, for *anything* to save him. He died the next day. Although this was a great disappointment to Lister, it did not shake his belief that carbolic acid could destroy germs that created blood poisoning, inflammation, and decaying flesh. He had yet to learn that once deadly germs got into a human's blood system, all the antiseptics in the world were of no help.

A second chance to test his theory of germs came to him some three months later. In July, a boy was brought into the surgical unit of the infirmary with his leg badly broken in two places where the wheels of a cart had run over it. After examining the wounds, Lister gently washed them clean with carbolic acid. Then he had the boy taken to the operating room and given an anesthetic before he carefully set the broken bones. During the trip to the operating room, and afterward, a cloth soaked with carbolic acid was kept over the wounds. When the boy was finally back in a ward bed, Lister issued strict orders that under no circumstances were any of the acid-soaked cloths to be removed from the wounds.

To make sure his orders would be obeyed, he carefully explained that lifting one of the soaked cloths for only a second's peek at the wound could provide enough time for germs to get into the wound and undo all his work. His orders were obeyed but few, if any, of the infirmary attendants and nurses took any stock in his theory that carbolic acid would destroy harmful germs in a wound and prevent postoperative setbacks. As a matter of fact, when it was learned what Lister was doing, his "fantastic" theory was ridiculed by many of Glasgow's medical men who had had far more years of experience than he.

In the case of the boy with the badly injured leg, however, Dr. Lister's "fantastic" idea worked out just fine. On the fourth day, Lister took off the carbolic-soaked cloths for a look at the wound. And what he saw made tears of thankful joy sting the backs of his eyes. The wounds were healing perfectly. There was no swelling at all, no inflammation of the skin; no stench of oozing, gangrenous pus. Scabs had formed over the wounds, and they were almost dry. The boy's leg, not to mention his life, had been saved, and in due time he was completely recovered from his terrible injury and able to leave the hospital on foot.

That second test was for Lister a complete success, but

it should be said that, unknown to him, luck played no small part. He had washed the wounds with carbolic acid before he reset the boy's broken leg bones, and afterward he had kept the wounds covered with cloths soaked in carbolic acid until they had healed sufficiently to form protective scabs. But while he was setting the broken bones he had taken no precautions at all. He had not washed his hands before operating, and he had not sterilized the instruments he used. He hadn't for the simple reason that in those days no surgeon gave so much as a thought to washing his hands, let alone sterilizing his surgical instruments. As a matter of fact, it was a practice not to wash one's hands, even after examining a patient, because so doing might offend the patient.

The complete recovery of the boy with the badly broken leg was a triumph for Joseph Lister, but in his mind only a very small one. After all it was one success. For all he knew, it could have been just a Heaven-sent stroke of pure luck. And success or not, the impression it had made on other surgeons in the hospital had been just about zero minus. It was still a crazy, fantastic theory as far as they were concerned.

So Lister set about proving again that he was right, but not with the idea of showing the skeptics. What others thought didn't bother him very much at the time. It was himself that he wanted to convince, beyond all possible doubt. So he made some more tests and they were successful, but they were cases not nearly as serious as the boy with the badly smashed leg. The doctor was, of course, pleased with the results, but he was still not convinced that his theory was one hundred per cent correct.

One day an injury case was brought into the hospital which at first glance seemed absolutely hopeless. The man was a laborer whose leg had been horribly mangled by a falling crate. To all but Dr. Lister there was only one thing to do if the man's life was to be spared: amputate the mangled leg at once. Lister, however, refused to amputate. Instead, he cleaned the man's wounds with carbolic acid and then took him to the operating room as he had taken the little boy. There he removed the countless bits of broken bone, and useless torn skin and flesh, and set the leg. As in the case of the small boy, he covered the wounds with cloths soaked in carbolic acid. This time he covered them with tinfoil to prevent evaporation of the antiseptic.

Then began the wait, with Lister's colleagues still insisting that he should amputate or the man would surely die. But Lister refused to do that, and after what must have seemed agonizing years to him, the fourth day arrived. He carefully removed the carbolic-soaked cloths and there before his eyes was the result for which he had fervently prayed. The grim wounds were healing nicely, and already beginning to scab over. Not a sign of telltale inflammation, and not a single symptom of gangrene setting in. Six weeks later the wounds were completely healed, and a short time after that the man was discharged from the infirmary fully recovered and able to walk again.

That success changed the opinions of a few of those

openly skeptical of Dr. Lister's work, but it still didn't satisfy him completely. In the case of the laborer with the horribly mangled leg he had tried something new. He had not only covered the acid-soaked bandages to prevent evaporation but had also, and for the first time in all medical history, washed his hands in a carbolic acid solution, and also the surgical instruments he intended to use. As a matter of fact, he had even wiped with a carbolic-acid-soaked cloth the strips of wood he used as splints for the man's broken leg. All those things, he felt sure, had contributed to the success of the test, but being something of a perfectionist he refused to accept it as an unqualified success. There was still room for improvement in his mind.

For one thing, if the carbolic acid was too strong it would destroy the germs in the wound, but it would also do harm to the torn flesh. In addition, a too-strong solution would burn and irritate the perfectly healthy skin around the wound. On the other hand, a carbolic acid solution that would not irritate the wound flesh or the surrounding skin might not be strong enough to do its job with the invading germs. That problem he eventually solved by adding a certain amount of linseed oil to the carbolic acid solution, which prevented outside irritation of the healthy tissues.

He also perfected the dressing put on open wounds. Instead of carbolic-soaked linen, he mixed carbolic acid with carbonate of lime to form a putty. This he placed over the wound, and he covered it with a sheet of tinfoil to prevent evaporation and also to form a firm protective cap over the wound. In addition to washing his hands and instruments in a carbolic acid solution, he also perfected a device with which he could spray the entire operating room with carbolic acid as an additional roadblock to existing germs.

In the next few months that followed, he made several more successful operations, employing the principle of antiseptics in surgery. Most of the cases that came into the hospital were compound fractures, but there were also abscesses to be lanced and drained, flesh wounds, and other cases. He gave each one, severe or light, his careful attention. And then came a day that was to mark the beginning of many years of frustration, embarrassment and annoyance for Joseph Lister.

Unknown to Dr. Lister, his wife had invited her father, Professor James Syme, who now occupied the Chair of Clinical Surgery at the University of Edinburgh, to make them a surprise visit. So when Lister arrived home from his infirmary one night there was his father-in-law to greet him and to advise him that the time had now come for Lister to make an official announcement of his great discovery in surgery. Until then, few medical men outside the University of Glasgow hospital knew anything about what Lister was doing, but James Syme was of the firm belief that now the entire British medical world should know. And he believed that the best way to tell the story was for Lister to write an article about his use of carbolic acid as an antiseptic and have it published in *The Lancet,* a widely read and highly respected medical journal, printed in London.

At first Dr. Lister was not inclined to agree with his father-in-law's idea. He had had several successes, but he had had one or two failures. And he was still not completely satisfied with the methods he used before, during, and particularly after the operation. There was still lots of room for improvement in many ways, so he did not think it was yet time for a published report on his work.

James Syme and his daughter, however, did think it was time, and in the end they were able to persuade Lister to write the detailed report. His wife helped him write it, and after mailing it off to *The Lancet* he promptly forgot it and returned to his work at the infirmary. But he was not to forget the report for very long!

The Lancet published his article, with carefully worded comments that both praised and damned his theory. It was received by the medical world with something less than enthusiasm, and this was partly the doctor's own fault. He had simply pointed out that carbolic acid used as an antiseptic was a safeguard against post-operative setbacks in cases of compound fractures. He did not make it clear to his readers that the whole idea of his tests had been to prove that the use of antiseptic *in any type of surgery* would, if administered correctly, prevent the usual hospital diseases of inflammation, blood poisoning and tissue decay.

That the readers of his article had missed the main point disheartened Lister and caused him to bitterly regret writing it at all. His father-in-law and his wife, however, were only angry at the stupidity of the readers and urged him to forget about it and continue with his work. Perhaps soon he would have the chance to prove his theory on some important operation that had nothing to do with compound fractures. He could then write, or give a lecture about it, and make it very plain that his theory applied to any type of surgery.

It so happened that a short time later he did perform an important operation. It was on a chronic abscess which had formed in front of the patient's spine. Up until then, that kind of an abscess was believed to bring almost certain death to the patient once it was opened and drained. Dr. Lister, however, felt certain that death was the result of germs getting into the cavity after it had been lanced, and when he did lance the patient brought to him, he kept the wound covered *at all times* with carbolic-solution-soaked material. Some of the other hospital surgeons who watched the operation became incensed at his "blind man's stab in the dark" method and declared he should be charged with criminal negligence if the patient died.

But the patient did not die. Once the infection had been lanced and drained, Dr. Lister replaced the acid-soaked linen with his "antiseptic putty" protective cap and let it remain there for several days before he lifted it and took a look at the abscess cavity. It was healing nicely, and continued to heal nicely. Six months later the miracle came to pass. A man normally doomed to almost certain death was discharged from the hospital in perfect health. And during all those six months there had not been one single symptom of any "usual" post-operative hospital diseases!

In the middle of August, 1867, the British Medical Association met in Dublin, Ireland, and one of the speakers on hospital surgery was Dr. Joseph Lister. He described his theory and his tests which proved it, particularly that important abscess operation. Sadly, he was no public speaker and his delivery did little to rouse the interest of the learned men who listened to him. But the main reason he failed to rouse any interest was because the vast majority simply refused to believe his claims. They thought his words just so much poppycock, and were not hesitant at all about saying so right to his face as he stood there on the speaker's platform. A few tried to defend him and get the others to consider seriously what he had told them, but their voices were but whispers in an increasing roar of scorn and emphatic disbelief.

Joseph Lister returned to Glasgow from that Dublin meeting a thoroughly frustrated and angry man, under the sting of his public humiliation. He believed he had made a discovery that would go far toward lessening the terror and agony felt by surgical patients and would help save countless lives that otherwise might have been lost. And yet, for his efforts, he had been sneered at and called a fraud.

Although Lister probably never thought of it at the time, what had happened to him was not at all unusual. It had happened before to others, and many times. Almost a hundred years before him, Edward Jenner had discovered a vaccine that prevented smallpox, but at first had the men high in medicine believed him? They had not! They had sneered at his fantastic claims and called him a crazy quack until he had proved beyond all possible doubt that his theory was fact and not fantasy.

Yes, that sort of thing had happened before to men who wanted only to serve mankind. Now it was Joseph Lister's turn to pit his faith in himself against the scorn and sneers of the professional critics.

And, as before, it took time. Getting the medical world to accept his discovery was not something Dr. Lister accomplished overnight, or even in a matter of months. He kept on with his work at the University of Glasgow, improving his techniques and making still other discoveries that helped to rid his hospital of postoperative setbacks which resulted in death. But no matter what he did, his critics continued to voice their disbelief.

In the latter part of 1869, he left Glasgow and returned to the University of Edinburgh to take the Chair of Clinical Surgery upon the retirement of its long-time holder, his father-in-law, Professor Syme. He continued his work there, and two years later the tide slowly started to turn in his favor. It was no less than Queen Victoria of England who changed the course of opinion. While visiting in Scotland the Queen had become bedridden with an extremely painful abscess, and she summoned Dr. Lister to attend her.

After examining the abscess he carefully explained what he was going to do, and why there would be no fatal aftereffects of the sort that usually occurred with that type of operation. The Queen listened intently and then told him to proceed. The operation was a complete success. Queen Victoria recovered completely from the operation, and a short time later it was announced that Dr. Joseph Lister had been appointed (Scottish) Surgeon to the Queen.

After that, medical acceptance of Dr. Lister's antiseptic theory began to snowball. Several prominent surgeons on the Continent began testing his theory and obtained surprising results. Surgeons in England slowly stopped heaping scorn on him and took some good hard looks at his theory themselves. Heartened by the approval his long years of work were now being given, Lister left the University of Edinburgh and deliberately took the post of surgeon in the small and more or less unknown King's College Hospital in London. The great men of surgery in London were still reluctant to accept his claims, so he went to their city so that they could see the results of his pioneering work for themselves.

At last the London doctors were convinced that Dr. Joseph Lister had indeed made one of the most exciting discoveries in all medical history. By 1890 the use of his antiseptic practices had rid almost every hospital in

Great Britain of pyemia, erysipelas and gangrene. And long before that time the doctor was receiving the high praise and reward he had so justly earned.

When he came to King's College in London, Queen Victoria appointed him Surgeon Extraordinary to Her Majesty, and in 1883 she made him a baronet. In 1897 the Queen increased his rank to that of Baron, which gave him the right to sit in the British House of Lords. Many other honors were showered upon Dr. Lister from all over the world, but in 1892 he was given an honor that pleased him more, perhaps, than all the others put together.

In that year, on December 27, the leaders of the French Republic, and the great men of chemistry, medicine and surgery from all over the world, met at the Sorbonne to pay tribute to Louis Pasteur. Joseph Lister was selected to represent Great Britain at that meeting, and it was one of the greatest joys of his life to be able to meet and warmly embrace the man who had given him the key to his own discovery that was to benefit all mankind.

9

The Magic of Mold

ALEXANDER FLEMING
(1881–1955)
HOWARD WALTER FLOREY
(1898–   )

On the morning of September 1, 1939, an announcer of the British Broadcasting Company interrupted a recorded music program to state that Adolf Hitler's Nazi legions had invaded Poland. The invasion of Poland was the start of World War II, which was to see millions on both sides die in battle, and many millions more be wounded before it was ended on September 2, 1945.

All that is well-known fact today, but something that is not so well known is that without the dedication and unswerving perseverance of two doctors, Alexander

[167]

Fleming and Howard Florey, countless numbers of those wounded in World War II might have been listed among the dead.

Their story ended in World War II, but it began before World War I. As a matter of fact, it could be said that it actually began when Alexander Fleming was born on a farm near Kilmarnock, Scotland, on August 6, 1881.

When he was old enough, young Fleming took a general course of study at the Kilmarnock Academy, and when he graduated, he went to London in search of a job. In London he worked at various occupations, but all the time he cherished a secret desire to enter the field of medicine. When he reached the age of twenty-one he decided to take the big step.

By good fortune, plus his own natural abilities, he was able to win a scholarship that entitled him to eight years of study as a medical student at St. Mary's Hospital Medical School. During those eight years he proved himself such a brilliant student that a few days after his graduation the head of St. Mary's Bacteriology Department, Sir Almroth Wright, offered him a job. Sir Almroth was well known for his research work on microbes, and during the four years that Fleming worked under him the younger man acquired an extensive knowledge of bacteria, antiseptics and vaccines.

At the end of those four years, World War I broke out, and Alexander Fleming entered the British Medical Corps. He was commissioned a captain and assigned to the British Expeditionary Force hospital at Boulogne,

France, for special duty. His job was to discover, if humanly possible, a wound antiseptic more effective than those then being used in the field.

All during the war he tested, checked and rechecked the effects of various chemicals on germs causing death. So did many other scientists, but by the end of hostilities in 1918 neither they nor Fleming had made any great progress. Some years before, the great bacteriologist, Paul Ehrlich, had expressed a firm belief that for every disease that afflicted man there must be a substance, a sort of magic bullet, that would seek out each particular germ and destroy it. Nevertheless, Captain Fleming's efforts during World War I didn't come anywhere near producing an antiseptic bullet that would seek out and destroy germs.

One thing he did learn, and the knowledge filled him with grave concern for wounded soldiers, sailors and airmen. One day, out of plain curiosity, he experimented with some of the well-known antiseptics—and some of those he and his colleagues had produced—on white blood corpuscles; in other words, on the human body's natural defense system against bacterial infection.

The results of those experiments both amazed him and frightened him. He discovered that some of the antiseptics being used were much better at destroying a human being's white blood corpuscles than they were at destroying the invading germs! In short, it was entirely possible that some wounded men had died from the effects of harsh antiseptics used to save them!

However, there appeared to be nothing Captain

Fleming or anybody else could do about this situation, and when the war ended, he returned to St. Mary's to pick up his work where he had left off at its outbreak. Ever in the back of his mind, however, was the unfortunate truth he had learned during his war service, and he repeatedly pledged himself to find a "magic bullet" that would destroy deadly germs without also causing injury to human tissues.

Whenever he could spare the time from his regular duties at St. Mary's he would conduct experiments and tests in quest of the substance he sought, and at the end of two years he was able to take a short step toward his goal. He found a microbe-dissolving chemical he called *lysozyme* that would destroy microbes. The only trouble was that the microbes *lysozyme* could destroy were not the types of microbes that caused diseases in human beings.

Nevertheless Dr. Fleming kept at his task, and at least he was able to work out a system by which he could determine the possible effectiveness of an antiseptic. The method was simple and sure. He would first determine how much of the antiseptic in question it took to kill certain microbes. Then he would determine how much of that same antiseptic it took to harm living white blood corpuscles. If it took less to harm white blood corpuscles than it did to destroy germs then that particular variety could be forgotten. But if it took more, than that particular antiseptic was well worth further experimentation and tests.

For another six years, Fleming's spare-time search

resulted in little success. However, he was establishing for himself the reputation of being an expert bacteriologist. He was made director of St. Mary's inoculation department, a well-deserved reward for his fine work at that institution. He was regarded as an expert not only on *staphylococci,* the grapelike clusters of deadly germs that infect the skin and mucous membranes, but also on *streptococci,* the chain-forming germs that attack the spinal cord, the lungs, the joints and the blood.

He wrote many papers on his work at St. Mary's and also on his spare-time search for what he called the "absolute antiseptic." And in 1928, as he was preparing to write a report about staphylococci, he discovered by sheer accident what he had been searching for during the last fourteen years.

Before actually writing his report, there were some experiments he wanted to make first. He had heard that under some conditions the grapelike clusters of staphylococci could be made to change their appearance, and he wanted to check this. The process he followed was to cover sterilized glass plates with sterilized jelly and shield them with sterilized glass tops. When several of the glass plates were prepared and covered he would whip off the glass covers one by one and place some staphylococci on the sterilized jelly, and re-cover it immediately. Then, each day after that, he would take the glass plates one by one and slide them under his dissecting microscope and observe the changes, if any, in the appearance of the planted germs.

He conducted this series of experiments for a number

of weeks, but those weeks happened to be summertime weeks and some of the windows in the laboratory were open—a lucky break for Dr. Alexander Fleming, and most certainly for countless numbers of soldiers, sailors and airmen who were going to be wounded in World War II! Had the doctor's laboratory been one of the gleaming and absolutely sterilized types to be found in institutions much more richly endowed than St. Mary's, the discovery he made might just possibly have never been made by anyone. But his laboratory was far from being one of the best, and in addition its windows were open that summer of 1928. So, luckily, an accident took place. . . .

It happened to one of the jelly-covered glass plates in which staphylococci had been planted. When he slid it under his dissecting microscope, he suddenly noticed something he had not observed on any of the other plates. For several minutes he peered at the greatly magnified grapelike cluster of germs, not at all sure his eyes weren't playing him tricks. On impulse, he called over his assistant and nodded at the microscope.

"Take a look, and tell me what you see," he directed.

Without a word the assistant put his eye to the viewing piece and took a good look.

"Well?" Fleming prompted, when the assistant finally straightened up with a frown. "What did you see?"

"I'm not sure," the man replied, still frowning. "There . . . there seems to be something growing on top of the staphylococci colony. Perhaps a mold, or something."

[172]

"Exactly," Dr. Fleming said. "It looks almost like a bit of bread mold. To me it looked white and fluffy, but with a bit of dark green color in the center."

"Yes, I saw that, too," the assistant murmured. "What do you think it is, and how did it get there?"

"What it is, I haven't the faintest idea," Fleming said with a shrug. "But it must have gotten there during the few seconds I had the cover off."

On impulse he turned and looked over at the opened windows and nodded slowly. "That's what did it," he said. "Or, let it happen, I mean. The breeze drifted some kind of spore in through one of those windows and it came to rest on the plate during the few seconds I had it uncovered. That must have been it."

"Must have," the assistant agreed. "And now it's contaminated that colony of staphylococci. So I guess we may as well throw that plate out. It's no good to you now."

"No, that one is ruined," Fleming agreed. "It's of no help to me now."

He started to remove the glass plate from under the microscope, but suddenly checked himself. Instead, he put his eye to the viewing piece and took another good look at the strange growth on the cluster of staphylococci. It was then that he saw something he had missed the first time he looked. The strange fluffy mold was *slowly dissolving the colony of staphylococci!* Around the bit of odd growth was a clear ring and on the outside of that clear ring more staphylococci were continuing to grow and multiply just as he had been observing

[173]

for weeks. But the deadly staphylococci covered by the green-centered mold were being slowly destroyed!

What was taking place before his eyes seemed like magic to Fleming. Could the mold be the magic bullet he had searched for all these years? He did not know, and at the moment he really didn't have anything on which he could even base a guess. But one thing was certain in his scientific mind: he certainly wasn't going to throw this contaminated plate away. Here was a bacteriological mystery of some sort, and he was determined to get to the bottom of it if he possibly could.

As a starter, to solve the mystery, he transplanted a bit of the strange growth to a fresh glass plate of microbes and discovered that it did the same thing—it grew, and as it grew it destroyed the microbe growth it covered. He transplanted the mold again and again and the results were the same. He put some of it in bottles of broth and watched what happened. For the first few days it grew white and fluffy on the surface of the broth. Then it slowly changed to a dark-green, fuzzy mass, and after a few weeks the broth turned a bright yellow.

At first Dr. Fleming thought that the yellow matter was what destroyed the staphylococci germs, but after some tests he found that his thinking was wrong. The mold juice, as he called it, would kill the germs of such diseases as meningitis, diphtheria and pneumonia, but it would do nothing to the germs of such diseases as cholera and typhoid. In short, the mold juice as he had prepared it was not a complete germ destroyer. There was some other substance secreted by the mold that was the complete germ killer when it was applied in sufficient strength. But the amount that had soaked into the mold juice he prepared was not strong enough.

Nevertheless the mold juice was a very powerful germ killer, even after being diluted as many as seven hundred times. Was it too powerful for human beings? Would it destroy human tissues and do far more harm than good? To find the answers to those questions, Dr. Fleming made tests on white blood corpuscles, and to his amazement found that the mold juice did not harm the blood cells at all. He also inoculated some rabbits with mold juice at its full strength, and the rabbits were not harmed in the slightest. In short his discovery was certain death to some lethal microbes, but seemed not at all harmful to human beings or animals.

Fortified with that knowledge, the doctor decided to make a test on a human being. He found two volunteers in one of St. Mary's wards, one with an infected wound and the other with an infected eye. He treated both with his mold juice, but unfortunately the tests did not result in one hundred per cent success. And the reason was something that Fleming had not yet been able to find out about his miracle mold juice. The quantity of mold juice he had prepared was not nearly enough. And as it had taken weeks for him and his assistant to prepare the small amount they did use, his two patients would either be cured by other means, or dead, long before he could prepare a sufficient quantity of the juice to give them a complete cure.

There were two other discouraging things that Dr.

Fleming and his assistant found out about their miracle mold. One was that it was quite fickle and would suddenly lose its strength for apparently no reason at all. And the other was that after relatively large quantities of the juice had evaporated, all that was left was a sticky mass from which it was impossible for them to extract whatever germ-killing chemical existed in its pure form. However, Fleming was able to give a name to his discovery. He was able to identify the strange mold as belonging to the penicillium family, and so he named it *penicillin.*

Unable to make further progress in determining exactly what was pure penicillin, he wrote a lengthy report on his years of searching for the will-o'-the-wisp magic bullet and had it published. Several well-known chemists, both in England and on the Continent, read it and conducted experiments with the mold, trying to extract the pure chemical, but with no more success than Fleming had.

Then in 1932 Alexander Fleming was forced to admit to himself that he had traveled along the road to the goal of his magic bullet as far as he could. True, he could have gone on, but he believed it would be a waste of effort and time because the internationally known chemical firm in Germany of I. G. Farbenindustrie had discovered a germ killer they called *prontosil.* It was later to become known as the first of the sulfa drugs, and although it was not a magic bullet that could destroy all types of germs, it could destroy many. Perhaps of even greater importance, it could be produced in tremendous quanties at relatively low cost.

And so Dr. Alexander Fleming abandoned his quest for the magic antiseptic germicide. In a sense he had come halfway, but it was now impossible for him to go all the way. There just wasn't the money, the equipment, and the large staff of chemists and bacteriologists needed to continue the work with any chance for success.

For Dr. Fleming a cure-all made of pure penicillin was a lost cause. But what he did not know, as he sadly returned to his regular work at St. Mary's, was that right then in England was a professor of pathology at the University of Sheffield who eight years later would tackle the task he had been forced to abandon, and eventually achieve the goal of his cherished dream.

The man's name was Howard Florey, and he had been born in Adelaide, Australia, in 1898. He was a brilliant student at Kyre College and St. Peter's Collegiate School, and in 1917, when Dr. Fleming was at the British hospital in Boulogne, France, seeking the perfect wound antiseptic, Florey enrolled in the medical school at the University of Adelaide. When he graduated he went to Oxford University in England as a Rhodes scholar, and then later to Cambridge University. He was a member of a scientific expedition that went to Spitzbergen, he studied further in the United States, and in 1926 he became associated with the London Hospital. And by 1932, the year that Fleming abandoned his quest for the magic cure, Howard Florey was a professor of pathology at the University of Sheffield, and one of the most highly regarded experts in his field.

In 1935 Dr. Florey was appointed to an even higher post. He was named professor of pathology at Oxford University, and that same year he met the man who was to become his co-worker in the penicillin battle and share in the eventual triumph.

To a certain degree it was none other than Adolf Hitler who made it possible for this meeting to come about. In 1933, Hitler had issued the orders to purge government, industry, law, medicine and science of Jews. As a result, thousands of Jews immediately fled Nazi Germany, and one of them was Ernst Boris Chain, twenty-seven years old, and born in Berlin. He had been doing brilliant work in the department of pathology at Berlin's Charity Hospital, where a great future seemed in store for him until Hitler's order. He fled to England and obtained a job in a Cambridge University laboratory headed by the famous Sir Frederick Gowland Hopkins. Two years later, in 1935, Howard Florey visited Sir Frederick at Cambridge to get his help in obtaining an expert chemist. Sir Frederick introduced him to Ernst Chain, and the two men were attracted to each other at first sight.

Florey and Chain quickly became a smooth-working team, with each man's store of scientific knowledge supplementing the other's, and one of the research jobs they eventually tackled was the new sulfa drugs. *Sulfanilamide* and its relatives were proving an amazing cure for certain diseases, but there were some for which none of the sulfa drugs had any curative powers. In short, the sulfa drugs were fine, the best bacteria destroyers known, but they were far from being the absolute germ killer.

As the result of their many experiments and tests, Florey and Chain decided to look for an antiseptic that would be deadly to all types of disease germs—in other words, the magic bullet that Alexander Fleming had searched for so many years before them. Because of other pressing work, they did not devote their time and efforts exclusively to their search. After all, they both realized it would undoubtedly take a great deal of time, even if they were fortunate enough to attain their goal.

In the autumn of 1939, when the BBC announced that Hitler had invaded Poland, there certainly was great cause for rush. England was bound to enter the conflict on the Continent in a matter of days, and her fighting forces would need the best of germ killers to save the lives of the countless numbers destined to be wounded. The best germ killer, however, was still unknown. It was the will-o'-the-wisp magic something they had been seeking in their spare time ever since the start of their association. Now that project took precedence over all others.

They started off by reading all the recent and old reports on bacteriological research they could get their hands on, and one of them was Alexander Fleming's detailed account of his discovery and research work on penicillin. The well-known bacteriologist's nine-year-old report intrigued and excited them. Penicillin? Was that it? But it still had to be tried and tested, and, above all, the pure penicillin had to be isolated, so that the full strength of its odd power could be obtained.

Almost certain that pure penicillin was the answer, they set to work immediately growing Dr. Fleming's mold. They enlisted the help of other chemists and pathologists, in their desperate fight against time, and in no time at all there were scores of highly trained men tackling the job that Fleming and his assistant had once attempted to do alone.

At length it was determined that penicillin was an acid, and that other acids could destroy it. They discovered that it existed in ether and in chloroform, and that it had a sort of crushed ripe pear smell. Best of all, Ernst Chain convinced himself by tests and experiments that if it could be reduced to dry, powdered form, it could be safely stored for unlimited periods of time.

By the end of eight months of intensive work, Florey, Chain and their numerous associates had gone far beyond the point where Alexander Fleming had stopped his work. In fact, they had succeeded in extracting a semi-purified form of penicillin from the mold growth. It was in the form of a brownish-colored powder, and when tested on infected rats, mice and cats it proved to be amazingly effective.

They made tremendous strides in those eight months, but they were still a long way from their goal. The war was also eight months old, and more soldiers were dying every day from infected wounds. Unfortunately, speed was something beyond the power of Drs. Florey and Chain right then. They had more or less found what they were seeking, but after eight long months of effort, the amount of penicillin they had been able to produce was just barely enough to make their vital tests on animals—not nearly enough for a critical test on a human being, and the crucial job was to take many months. In fact, it was not until the early part of 1941 that they produced the amount they thought they needed. True, in the meantime they had succeeded in extracting a variety of penicillin that was much more pure than had been the original product—and they learned that the power of what they were now extracting was almost unbelievable. It was still a mighty germ killer even after it had been diluted thousands of times.

It was February of 1941 when the researchers treated their first human being with penicillin. The patient was a policeman with a sore at one corner of his mouth, which had continued to spread in spite of the sulfa drugs used to treat him. He was mortally ill, because the deadly infection had already affected his skin, lungs, bones and blood.

The man selected to administer penicillin to the policeman was Dr. Charles Fletcher, and he did so at intervals of three hours. At the end of twelve hours the patient seemed to be holding his own, and at the end of twenty-four hours his condition showed a remarkable improvement. Three days after the first injection of penicillin it was evident that the magic mold was saving the man from the grave.

The new wonder drug performed its amazing job of germ killing for five days. Each day the policeman's condition showed remarkable improvement. And then —there was no more penicillin. The amount needed for his case was too great. The small stockpile of penicillin had been used up. There was not enough time left to produce more, and a few days later the policeman sank back to his original condition, and died.

Despite their discouragement in this case, Florey and Chain now knew beyond all doubt that if sufficient penicillin could be injected into a patient for a long enough period of time, his life could be saved. Their purpose now was to be able to produce penicillin in great quantities.

One hurdle was cost. It was estimated that the cost of treating that one policeman with penicillin for five days had been five thousand dollars a day. At that rate, the cost of treating thousands of war-wounded men in desperate need of penicillin would be, to say the least, astronomical. Also, the work involved in production was out of all proportion. It required forty gallons of carefully prepared mold juice and close to two weeks of patient work to produce enough pure penicillin to treat one patient for only one day. In short, it appeared to Florey and Chain that they had reached the end of their road. But they simply could not give up. There was war raging all around the world.

The researchers had to keep trying, and they did. They enlisted more scientists in their great cause, they obtained large sums of money, and they succeeded in getting a major British chemical company to attempt to produce penicillin in its laboratories. With all working at top speed, a sufficient amount was finally made to make a check test on another patient. This time there was enough. After seven days of treatment the patient was cured of a deadly infection. But the Herculean task of producing penicillin in quantity was still to be accomplished, and by then the German Luftwaffe was making that task seemingly more hopeless of accomplishment. All England was being plastered with bombs, and factories, laboratories and chemical plants that might have been able to help the penicillin team were being destroyed from the air.

There was only one place, now, where Florey and Chain could obtain the tremendous amount of help they needed, and that was the United States.

In the summer of 1941 Dr. Howard Florey arrived in the United States. Although the time was before Pearl Harbor, those in government were pretty sure that, just as in World War I, the United States was bound to get into the fight sooner or later. For that reason, Florey's desperate appeal for help with his problem did not fall on deaf ears. The work he was doing with penicillin had not gone unnoticed on this side of the Atlantic, and in a relatively short time after his arrival, a mighty team of United States chemists, bacteriologists and other specialists were hard at work.

How long it would take and what it would cost to produce the millions upon millions of penicillin units needed, nobody knew or cared to make a guess. There was a vitally important job to be done, and that was all that mattered. It is now known that before the job was completed the British and American governments spent close to a hundred million dollars.

During the first year of that all-out effort, mold was grown in huge vats, and an intensive search was made for other types of mold that might contain penicillin, while the methods of extracting it and purifying it were constantly improved. But by the end of that first year only a very small amount of the wonder drug had been produced for further checking purposes. All during that time, thousands of civilian and military doctors all over the world were begging for it so that lives might be saved.

In 1943, however, the research and production program began to pick up speed. Two new molds had been discovered that would produce much more penicillin than the ones then being used. One was found in a laboratory collection of molds, and the other was found growing on a fruit market's cantaloupes! It was also discovered that when a certain type of fluid left over from the making of starch was fed to regular mold growth, it increased the mold's penicillin content as much as nine or ten times.

The amount of pure penicillin produced by the beginning of 1943 totaled only something around a hundred million units, equal to about two ounces of the drug—enough for the treating of only a hundred and fifty patients. But by May the total output had reached four hundred and twenty-five million units, and when it climbed to seven hundred and sixty million units in July, hopes for winning the desperate race against time began to soar.

THE MAGIC OF MOLD

Of course, as the output of pure penicillin increased, so did the demand for it. The entire world was now ablaze with war, and the number of wounded who might be saved by penicillin increased alarmingly every day. There was no letting up for those on the penicillin production lines. They worked harder than before, if that were possible, and in the meantime, teams of doctors went to various places in the world to make on-the-spot tests with the wonder drug.

Dr. Howard Florey himself went to Africa to test penicillin on wounded Allied soldiers evacuated from the invasion of Sicily. He made his tests not only in hospitals but under conditions of intense heat, dust and swarming flies. The results were absolutely amazing. Dr. Alexander Fleming's great dream during World War I had become a reality in World War II. There now was a magic bullet that would destroy deadly germs anywhere in the human body.

Not only had the magic medicine been discovered, but the problem of mass production had also been licked. During the crucial year of 1943, penicillin production increased from one hundred million units to close to two billion units. By the time the war ended in 1945 the output figure was a trillion units, or about a thousand pounds per month!

Because of the dedicated efforts of Alexander Fleming, Howard Florey, Ernst Chain and a thousand helpers, penicillin saved the lives of countless fighting men in World War II, and it is saving the lives of thousands of people all around the world today.

The Author

ROBERT SIDNEY BOWEN was born in Boston, Massachusetts. During World War I he was an ambulance driver
for the American Field Service, and then took to the air
as a fighter pilot with the British Royal Air Force. In
1928 he was editorial director of the International Aero-
nautics Conference in Washington, D.C.

A veteran reporter, he worked for the *London Daily
Mail,* the Paris edition of the *Chicago Tribune* and two
Boston newspapers. He has edited the *Marine Journal,
Motor World Wholesale, Flying News* and *Aviation
Magazine* and written innumerable short stories and
novelettes, plus seventy-three books. His adventurous
background and vast experience with deadlines qualified
him for his radio script-writing job on "Terry and the
Pirates" and "Major North of Intelligence."

Now living in Jacksonville, North Carolina, Mr.
Bowen has four children and five grandchildren.